BOATING - EXPOSED!

Mis-Adventures Ashore and Afloat

Bill Kaster

Cartoons by: Bob Cleland

BOATING - EXPOSED!

Bill Kaster

Published By:
Puget Sound Press
6523 California Ave., S.W.
PMB 292
Seattle, WA 98136-1833
http://www. pugetsoundpress.com
email: thezo@sprintmail.com

ISBN: 0-9660092-5-8
Library of Congress Catalog Number: 99-67411

Cover design by: Dean Ingram
Cartoons by: Bob Cleland
All art work, graphics, and cartoons are the property
of Bill Kaster and Bob Cleland.

Printed in the United States of America

1 2 3 4 5 6 7 8 9

Mr. Boatperson's helpful hint on anchoring technique for both sail and powerboaters:

"Anchoring? Not too bad for the first attempt ever, but could stand some improvement. Basically, as shown here, it's the wrong way to do it. Do not attempt this with your boat."

Mr. B.

ABOUT BOATING-EXPOSED!

When two-time Liars Club award winner Bill Kaster sets his sights on boating, the unexpected expectedly happens. This playful parody lightly roasts recreational boating from its historical roots to the future.

This collection of short stories and sketches, intended for boaters, once-upon-a-time boaters, would-be and wannabe boaters, non-boaters and people who may have seen a boat at some time in their lives, either accidentally or on purpose and who shall be labeled "landlubbers," is a work of fiction. It is the product of the author's wild imagination and mild nightmares. Any and all person's names, any quotes and incidents, and most place names appearing herein are to be considered coincidental and fictitious in nature and intent. However, considering the vast multitudes of people on planet Earth today, it is actuarially possible for names, quotes, and some of the incidents found here to be represented by real, living people and events, although the quotes and incidents would represent almost miraculous circumstance, perhaps in a parallel universe. For any living or dead person who finds his or her name herein, the author offers sympathy and condolences, but simply think of it as free advertising for yourself. And let's be truthful: Not everyone gets even one opportunity to get his or her name in print, and in a book, yet! So, congratulations!

San Grande Island, home of the Happy Hills Hospital and Rest Home, takes its place along-side such other mythical sites as Shangri-La, Bali Ha'i, Brigadoon, and the lost city of Atlantis, as the characters play out their roles. These tongue-in-cheek stories will guarantee smiles throughout, and perhaps some chuckles, loud guffaws or horse laughs. The astute reader may even gain knowledge of what NOT to do in a boat or on a dock, on the beach or in the water.

ABOUT THE AUTHOR

Seattle native Bill Kaster has never been far from the lakes, rivers, and salt water of the Pacific Northwest. His first home as an infant was one of the original houseboats on the north shore of Lake Union. A University of Washington graduate in education, a combat veteran of the Korean War, and longtime power and sailboater, Bill has enjoyed a career as teacher and athletic coach in the area's public schools. An apparent mutation in gene #764 has enabled him over the years to see most of life's happenings in a joyful light, although some detractors would substitute "weird" for joyful. You may judge for yourself as you read.

ABOUT THE ARTIST

Bob Cleland, professional cartoonist, has lived in the Pacific Northwest for 36 years. Also a career teacher and successful athletic coach, Bob's multiple talents have extended onto the operatic stage as a baritone, for many years, with Seattle Opera. He continues to draw cartoons for parties, private gatherings, and cultural events. Bob's playful and witty art work, scattered throughout this book, brings extra good cheer and animation to what otherwise would have been just a lengthy series of black words printed on white paper.

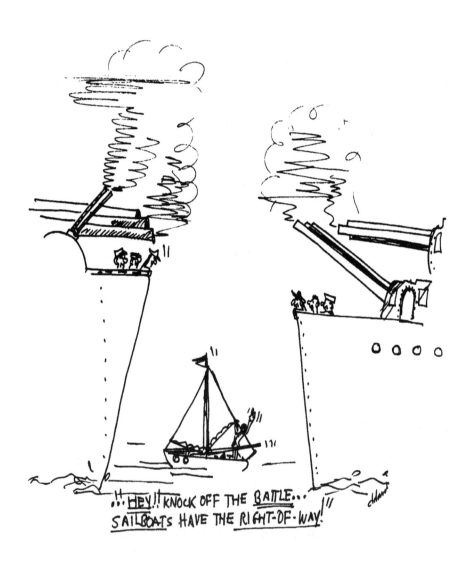

A WARNING TO ANYONE WHO WRITES!
(Amplification of page ii)

Note: Before reading this section, please read the fine print of page ii FIRST. This is very important for you.

Despite *Boating-Exposed!* having been classified as "certifiably crazy," as well as the author, it is imperative that you use NO PART of it or reproduce ANY part of it without the author's express permission, in writing! Perchance he should give permission, there is now a usage fee for any part, word, phrase, or sentence used by you that is found in the book. There is ONE exception: A reviewer writing a good book review may use part or parts with no charge. NOT included in this exception are reviewers writing negative reviews.

The following is just a tiny sampling of words that may NOT be used in your writing, all being classified as PART of *Boating-Exposed!*. For clarification, see Note #2 below. a, am, against, and, are, as, at, be, been, being, by, for, from, geoduck, had, has, have, him, her, hers, it, its, it's, me, mine, of, only, or, so, that, their, theirs, they, they're, them, this, to, too, was, were, when, which, we, who, whom, why, what, you, your, yours.

For the complete list of banned words, all found in *Boating-Exposed!*, send $18.00 in small, unmarked bills to the author at Happy Hills. No checks, money orders, cashier's checks, or credit card numbers will be accepted. The 255-page list of banned words, when received, should be kept by your side while writing to avoid a very large lawsuit for copyright infringements of various sorts.

Note #2: In the 1998 Supreme Court decision, Literary World vs. Kaster, the Court, by an 8-1 decision in his favor, ruled that the wording "No part of this book" should be taken to mean "NO part of this book," with the key phrase being "NO PART." Clearly, the justices reasoned, individual words constitute important, nay, essential parts, for without words, a book would merely be a glued collection of empty white sheets of paper, probably having little, if any, literary merit for readers, who might become discouraged looking at page after page of clean, white sheets. Several justices initially thought that these sheets could be used to draw pictures on, but as a regular package of paper costs so much less than a book of white sheets, this idea was soon dropped.

The dissenting justice argued that these words, now in effect granted to the author as his own, are so commonly used from early childhood through adulthood, that barring use by anyone other than the defendant would result in the total collapse of the American educational system, world wide business communities, scientific research, and the exploration of space. The reply by the eight justices was a curt "Inevitable, but legal, and now the law of the land." This was taken by the violent opponents of the decision to mean, "Tough, so what're you going to do about it?" or "That's the way the cookie crumbles." Hard feelings ran high, and harsh words were spoken by both sides.

In a pending appeal, the author is being asked to drop/alter/limit his victory to include only authors of books, magazine articles, and journalists in the newspaper industry. If this appeal is granted, at least elementary school student writers would be kept from lawsuits after writing essays on "What I did on my Summer Vacation," and like works ordinarily found in both public and private schools. The decision as it now stands has legal implications for small school boys carving such things as "I luv Annie" onto their wooden desk tops, as both "I" and "Luv," a schoolboy variation of "love," are on the complete list of banned words, and the boys are writing, though in an unusual fashion.

The author is seriously considering settling for around a sum of $30,000,000, a mere pittance compared to the tens upon tens of millions, perhaps billions, of dollars he would have received in usage payments from writers for his permission to use the words he now protects as his own intellectual properties. If a settlement is not made, he has agreed, out of the goodness of his heart, to provide hot dogs, soft drinks, and portable toilets for the 90,000-160,000 authors, writers, and journalists expected to march against, surround, and blockade the Department of Justice Building in our nation's Capitol next month, in protest, should the Court's decision be allowed to stand.

TO THE BROWSER —
WHY SHOULD YOU BUY BOATING-EXPOSED!?

As you stand here at the bookshelf browsing, the question naturally arises: Why should I buy this particular book, rather than another? What sets it distinctly apart, aside from its imparted wisdom, deep insights into human nature, witty repartee and dialogue-to-die-for, rib-tickling humor, and intelligently developed themes, practical solutions to everyday problems, and fresh looks at historical events? Other than these few, paltry reasons, here are others that will convince you that *Boating-Exposed!* belongs in an honored place on your bookshelf at home:

*It has been written for today's men and women, the on-the-go readers who can snatch five minutes here, ten minutes there, to enjoy reading.
*To help save time for those precious moments you do have to read, the author has incorporated a host of new techniques to make that time memorable:
*It has been tested and proved conclusively by Professor M. Strawbridge, Senior Research Scientist of West Eastchester College-in-the-Field, U.K., that all readers' brains momentarily STOP WORKING each time their eyes encounter a period at the end of a sentence, much like a car driving down a street containing many stop signs. The brain must then, like a computer, gather enough energy to commence the start of the next sentence, consequently tiring both the readers' brains and bodies. These startling research results have been confirmed by independent laboratories in seven countries, and have been incorporated into the writing of this book by:

Writing long, rambling sentences, thereby eliminating 60% to 70.8% of all the periods that would have been used by writing shorter, more uninteresting ones.
Writing the entire book using no punctuation marks whatsoever including commas which slow down but don't stop brain processing as periods do the editor and publisher took an avid position against this idea initially but when it was pointed out by the author

that the no-punctuation format would be more than offset by the critical-thinking process on the part of readers trying to figure out what was being written they saw the strength of this argument and agreed to pioneer it environmentally the no-punctuation format becomes very important by reducing the amount of ink used by the periods and commas thus saving our planet's precious resources available now in better office supply stores everywhere are adhesive-backed periods and commas in eight bright colors including your basic black for the traditionalists such as english teachers the loud screams of anguish are coming from english teachers and grammarians who would have to find something else to teach instead of period and comma usage and to a lesser extent colons and semicolons because they're used less frequently the careful reader may have already noticed that this section appears in this latest style as a sample of how your children's school books will be printed in future years see how rapidly you scanned this section we are honored to have had prof. strawbridge join us at happy hills where he is able to continue his research in total isolation away from the jealous taunts and jibes of his detractors his latest project is developing a system that eliminates capital letters thus saving typists everywhere valuable time by not having to depress the shift key you may have noticed a sample in this section he would be glad to have any visitors seriously interested in his research but due to the lengthy periods of convalescence following each of his treatments his visiting hours are restricted to thursday afternoons and then for only two hours.

Editor's and Publisher's Note: After initially agreeing to print this entire book without any punctuation marks, we both, after struggling through the preceding section, felt a mistake in judgement had been made. While the no-punctuation format has obvious advantages for advanced readers, the average and sub-average readers might become overly challenged, intimidated, and frustrated, thereby hurting book sales and our good reputation. It simply didn't seem to be the right time to initiate the Professor's vision for the future of reading.

We flew to Happy Hills to discuss our decision with the author to go with the standard punctuation that most readers have come to know and love, having learned it in stimulating classes at school.

Fortunately for us, the author was in arm and leg restraints that day, so, by a vote of 2-1 it was democratically voted upon to print the book our way.

However, we did leave the no-punctuation-capitalization section in to show the possible style your children will face as the style catches on and enjoys a popular growth. We are proud to announce that in order to be the first to test these waters, we are now preparing the author's next novel in this proposed style. It is an intriguing true story of his abduction by aliens, his individual battle to conquer their planet and civilize them, and his ultimate escape from their clutches by riding a passing comet back to Earth. Look for it soon at better bookstores everywhere. As a special bonus, the first 500 buyers will be given a FREE packet of 1,000 adhesive-backed punctuation marks, in assorted colors, to be placed in the book wherever desired.

More reasons to buy *Boating-Exposed!:*

*No more wimpy, large-sized, easy-to-read letters and words! By reading this size print, your eye muscles will strengthen, enabling you to amaze your eye doctor at your next eye appointment with at least 20/15 vision. The happy day you are able to throw away your glasses or contacts for good you will bless me. But there are many other, widespread advantages to be found in every walk of life:
*For students - For the first time, you'll be able to see and decipher the words your teacher has written on the blackboard. You'll be able to see and copy test answers from that smart kid across the aisle from you without squinting, a dead giveaway to teachers looking for cheats like you.
*For the sickly - You'll be able read and understand your doctor's handwriting. Never again will you have to search around the house for a magnifying glass to read the instructions on the medicine bottles.
*For scientists - Throw away those heavy, costly electron microscopes! With the improvement of your eyes from reading *Boating-Exposed!* you'll be able to spot and identify disease-producing germs, viruses, bacteria, and allergens at a glance, growing on the agar plates in your labs. Astronomers will see black holes, and

researchers worldwide will be able to swat and eliminate the germs of cholera, tuberculosis, malaria, and hoof-and-mouth disease, just to name a few examples.

*For drivers - You'll spot police-generated impulses from radar guns before they hit your car and rebound back for registry on the meter readout. No more speeding tickets! Right there I've saved you a bundle in fines. You should buy this book in appreciation, if nothing else.

*For boaters - You'll see buoys, landmarks, whales, and on-rushing foreign freighters bearing down on you through the fog. On a dock, you'll be able to spot bird, dog, or seal poop long before stepping in it. You won't, however, see any of those gorgeous models who pose in skimpy swimsuits for boating ads. They're all inflatable, and kept in boxes in warehouses in California and Florida during off-seasons.

*For parents - Save HUGE dollar amounts by fashioning paper toys out of the virtually indestructible pages of this book. Paper airplanes, boats, hats, and origami projects will make enjoyable and much-sought-after birthday and Christmas gifts for your kids, replacing those expensive dolls, action figures, noisy guns, trikes, bikes, skates, and games. Your kids will love their paper toys, after a period of adjustment, usually not much more than two or three years. With the savings, you can then spend BIG BUCKS on outfitting your boat properly, something you couldn't do before the purchase of this book.

*For homeowners- Every home has chair and table legs of unequal length. By snipping out the exact thickness necessary from this book, you can stabilize the offending piece of furniture without creating an unsightly dent in your linoleum. And if you snip out the correct number of pages needed from the blank space margins, you'll still have text to read, adding even more enjoyment as you are now able to follow the stories without having to guess what the author might have written.

*For campers - Buy a copy to take along on your next campout. The pages are guaranteed to ignite and produce a hot flame, eliminating your having to search for kindling, a blessing in such places in Western Washington's beautiful campgrounds, where, historically, no camper has ever been able to find dry wood for kindling. These burning pages do NOT produce dangerous, flying sparks, unlike wooden kindling, which generally sets the entire forest on fire, ruining your camping trip. Buy two!

The final time-saving feature of *Boating-Exposed!* represents the grandest and most advanced concept for time-starved readers known today. The book is 94% free of all words constructed of four or more syllables! With so many words of only one, two, or three syllables, think how quickly you'll race through chapters, unfettered by wading through many slow-you-down words such as pro-cras-tin-a-tion, en-vi-ron-ment and ap-pre-ci-a-tion. Professor Strawbridge has, on display here at Happy Hills, his condensed version of *War and Peace*. This has been an ongoing project of his since 1958 and includes all the time-saving techniques with which you have just become acquainted, plus a few more, certain to take the literary world by storm. His blockbuster research on *War and Peace* is given here, for the first time! He has given the book's many characters American names, such as Joe, Bob, Sam, Tom, Bev, Ann, and Kit.

These replace all the Russian names found in the book, such as Semyonovsky, Konovnitsin, Dmitrievna and Feraponotoff, which not only take up a lot of space in that book, but also tend to confuse and slow down non-Russian readers. Then he eliminated the war scenes, peace scenes, and love scenes, while still maintaining the flavor and excitement of the original classic.He alsotriedrunning allthewordstogethertosavespacebutthepublicandemoniumand outcry againsttthisprocedurecauseedhimtoburnthecopyandyoucanseewhy aftertryingtomakesenseofthisentence. I mean, we have to draw the line somewhere! He has this new, condensed version now on sale, reduced from over 850 pages to 16. The fact that he used print this size may have helped somewhat in the condensation. To stimulate sales, he is offering, at 50% off, your choice of a low-powered microscope or a powerful hand-held magnifying glass to help you wade through the volume, plus a free bottle of the headache remedy of your choice. Buy now!

Well, there you have it. Compelling, healthful, and money and time-saving reasons to buy *Boating-Exposed!*. Still undecided? Do the following before you put it back on the shelf. Stare, no wavering, for one minute at the black dot

●

Now, repeat to yourself aloud: "I am getting sleepy. I will see, hear, or think of nothing that will keep me from buying *Boating-Exposed!*. I will take this book with me to the front sales counter and give the cashier the amount asked for. If I don't have money enough with me to buy the book, I will go to my bank, withdraw enough money to buy it, return to the bookstore, buy it, take it home, read it, and tell all my friends about it, except for the dumb parts. I will not lend this book to any of my friends. They must buy copies for themselves. If I overhear anyone counting to ten by ones, I will snap out of this trance and appear normal again, unlike most of the book's characters."

BOATING-EXPOSED!
What Others are Saying

"*Boating-Exposed!?* It looks like a book. It feels like a book. The pages can be turned, one after the other, like a book. In my opinion it is definitely a book."

Stanley Podemkin, Book Reviewer
Los Angeles Moon Times

"If I had stayed at home that night to read *Boating-Exposed!* instead of going to Ford's Theater, I might still be President."

A. Lincoln, Past President, U.S.A.
Room 1414, Happy Hills

"*Boating-Exposed!?* I have ordered my supply sergeants to confiscate all copies from bookstores and distribute them to all my troops. Reading it will raise their morale, enabling my infantry and cavalry to defeat the British and General Wellington at Waterloo next month."

Napoleon B., Grand Marshal & Emperor
Room 1429, Happy Hills

"A life saver! *Boating-Exposed!* was in the left breast pocket of my field jacket as I led the charge to the top of San Juan Hill. Not only did it stop two bullets fired at me, but it also became useful later when the regiment ran out of toilet paper. Then, by reading it, rather, what was left of it, I found my mind became quite focused on my subsequent presidential bid. One might very truthfully say that I owe a lot to this book."

Teddy R., Past President, U.S.A.
Chairman, Bull Moose Party
Room 1903, Happy Hills

"As I sit here on Dad's right side, I hereby verily sayeth unto ye men and women of good faith. Firstly, read and memorize the Good Book. Then, read *Boating-Exposed!* It will be required reading for admittance through the Pearly Gates. Be prepared to give a five-minute oral summarization and your comments and analysis on both books upon reaching the Admissions Office when thou arriveth."

Jesus C., CEO-Admissions Office
Room 1721, Happy Hills

"Hey-a, Paisano! My-a boys will-a be-a comin' to you-a house soon. Dis-a my-a territory. You- buy-a de book...Right? No? How-a you-a like-a to go deep-a sea trip in-a cement-a boots? Get-a de picshur? Boys will-a tell-a you how-a much to-a pay. Small-a unmarked-a bills only. T'ank-a you. Good a-doin' beezness wit-a you."

Santiello F., Godfather
Room 812, Happy Hills

"Review is good...brilliant first book...good sense...dynamite...Will take its place among classic literature...great author...I like this!...demand is high...don't delay...buy soon."

Gordon Uplate, President & CEO
New Generation Book Analysis, Inc.
New York, New York

"This comedy of errors, a winter's tale, appears at first as much ado about nothing. As you like it, the tempest becomes as an eagle-winged pride of lofty thoughts, yet dastardly action. Forsooth! Fly thee hence, beauteous ink, and as fresh-visaged youth becomes vintaged as a cracked and faded yellowing pot, measure for measure these unruly tales topple down steeples and moss-grown towers, but not yet monolithic works such as mine. Ply pen to paper, Varlet, thine faint, scarce chance to replace the Bard, myself, as vapors in the breeze appear as nothing. Yet, by yon bright light........."

W. Shakespeare, Bard
Room 257, Happy Hills

Shakey: Sorry to cut you off now just as you were getting warmed up, but we are facing space limitations here. Thanks for your input. I left three reams of paper, ink, and a quill pen in your room in case you want to start another writing project. How about a sequel to King Henry VIII? You could call it, let's say, King Henry IX. The public is clamoring for more Henry stories. You might even become famous some day.

P.S. Where'd you put your volumes of King Henry I, II, III, and VII? The occupant of room 712 wants to read the entire Henry series.

P.S. 2. We're having trouble getting enough goose fat for making the special ink you require. Let me know if crow, robin, or sparrow fat will work just as well. I know you write best early in the morning but are bothered by those crows, Will it help you to concentrate if there are fewer of them around? Let me know. Supervisor, Happy Hills

Editor and Publisher
Happy Hills Press
6 Milipon Drive
Floraton, San Grande Island - AN-36

Ladies and Gentlemen:

It has been suddenly and forcefully brought to my attention that Bill Kaster, whom you have unfortunately taken under your wing, has taken extreme liberty with a letter I wrote to him several months ago. It was in regards to a request he had made of me to recommend his book, *Boating-Exposed!.* As you are well aware, my book rating service is highly regarded among authors, and we do hundreds of readings yearly, giving our opinions, which can be highly stimulating to the success or failure of these books. I, in effect, slammed his book, downgrading it to the nth degree. Yet, what appeared on the "What Others are Saying" pages of the book when it came out in print gives exactly the opposite impression to readers from what I conveyed to him. I am enclosing a copy of my original letter to Mr. Kaster, with the words, shown in italics in it, that actually appeared in the letter, supposedly from me, which, as you can see, are completely opposed to what I intended.

Sincerely yours,

Gordon Uplate

Gordon Uplate, CEO
New Generation Book Analysis, Inc.
New York, N.Y.

Bill Kaster, Room 1211
Happy Hills Rest Home
6 Milipon Drive
Floraton, San Grande Island, AN-36

Dear Mr. Kaster:

I have *reviewed* your book, *Boating-Exposed!*. It *is* not *good* news,
but I hope it does not discourage you from attempting other works of
fiction in the future. It is not a *brilliant first* novel, as we have come
to expect from other *book*s written in the solitude of Happy Hills. It
probably should have been wrapped up by people of *good sense*
and *dynamite*d into oblivion. I *will take* that first step, if asked, to
detonate the dynamite and return the book to *its* best *place, among*
the rest of today's claptrap. The *classic literature* of the past is in no
danger, *I* know, from tripe *like this*! I would *demand* an apology from
you for sending th*is* juvenile attempt to me. There are too many
false, misleading statements and wild exaggerations! I have *high*
hopes that you *don't delay* in correcting these grievous errors in
future books. Otherwise, many more unsuspecting readers will *buy
soon*, wasting both their time and money.

Best regards,

Gordon Uplate

Gordon Uplate, CEO
New Generation Book Analysis, Inc.
New York, N.Y.

P.S. We have published several books in the King Henry series.
W. Shakespeare is near you there. Ask him for help.

CONTENTS

CONTENTS (cont.)

BOATING WISDOM FROM THE PAST

To draw from the wisdom of the past seems appropriate for creating links with one's own boating ancestors. To show the relationship more personally, I have included the following boat-related quotes that will bring a long-lost past into your present. The French and German thoughts were found painted on cave walls, the Italian from a dry, cracked goat-skin leather parchment, the Babylonian from a hardened clay tablet, the Polish from the cambium (inner bark) layer of a cedar tree, and the Russian from a carved, 98-carat ruby on the crown of an ancient czar. The anonymous quote is dated relatively recently, taxes not becoming prohibitive until the 1950s, but the reference to *Boating-Exposed!* places it closer to 1999, when the book was written.

To gain the full feeling of peace and serenity from the ancients, the translations have been placed at the end of the collection. Even if you are not acquainted with the language quoted, simply repeat each one aloud as you come to it, remembering that someone, perhaps an ancestor of yours, said it before you. You have shared in the past! (Remember that the ancient standards of language usage were quite informal in those times, when most people had more to worry about than if what they said was grammatically correct.)

"Canotage? Un barque est passionant, bien, mais tout couteux, mais vivre, fabrication amour, nous trouver, est seulement mieux!"
French cave graffiti, circa A.D. 1285

"Lecture autour canotler est bien."
French cave graffiti, circa A.D. 1285

"Die See ist sehr ruhig, aber du das Buchen lesen, es machen sie lacheln und lachen. Aber ven die See ist harsch, fallen lassen das Buch und das Boot steueren."
German motto, cave graffiti, circa A.D. 410

1

"A petrece lune, niciodate a conduce barca pe nisip plaja, prost!"
Romanian proverb, circa A.D. 650

"Qual e la temperatura dell acqua? Eruscaldata? Si puo nuotare senza pericolo? Smettere! Tenga le mani a posta!"
Italian beach parchment, circa 880 B.C.

"Sono speacente. Scusi, la nausea. Dov a l'ippodromo piu vicino? Arrivederci!"
Italian parchment from Roman newspaper interview. The interviewer had asked whether the interviewee enjoyed boating. Probably why the Italian navy is short of naval recruits. Circa 140 B.C., but awaiting carbon-14 dating to pinpoint exact date.

"MeH R Towhnt. Tya er, Kak MOXO cKOpee!!!!
Russian, from ruby carving, circa A.D. 108

Cuneiform from Babylonian clay tablet, circa 2100 B.C.

"Jeden dobry lodz I jeden dobry ksiazka? Niebianski kiedyz rownoczesnie lodz uczucie I ma wywracac."
Polish traditional bark carving, circa A.D. 785

Having just assimilated the warmth not only of the native language as written, but of rolling the language orally through your vocal cords and off your tongue, the figurative translations are hereby offered:

French: "Boating? A boat is exciting and good, but quite expensive. Making love, we find, is even better!"
French: "Reading aboard a boat is good!"
German: The sea is very calm, and when you read a book aboard, it makes you smile and laugh. But when the sea becomes rough, drop the book and steer the boat!"

Romanian: "To enjoy oneself while boating, never steer the boat onto a sandy beach, stupid."

Italian: What's the temperature of the water? Is it heated? Is it safe for swimming? Stop! Keep your hands to yourself!"

Italian: "I'm sorry. I get nausea. Where's the nearest race track? Arrivederci!"

Russian: "I am seasick! Get me to a toilet quickly!"

Babylonian: Where's the water? I'm stuck on this sandbar!"

Polish: "A good boat and a good book. Heavenly when they are together, unless the boat has capsized and is sinking!"

American Modern (?): "A smile, chuckle, or hearty laugh from reading *Boating-Exposed!* is much better than reading IRS tax forms and real estate tax assessments!"

Toilet stall graffiti, circa A.D. 1999

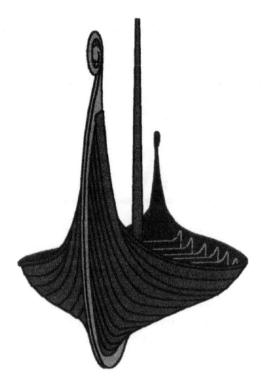

small viking boat

ADDENDUM: BOATING'S CONTRIBUTIONS TO THE ADVANCEMENT OF CIVILIZATION
A Scholarly Essay

From the previous section, the careful reader, unknowingly perhaps, has been privy to the dramatic growth in the sophistication of the written language. Examine again the apparently crude, wedge-shaped cuneiform quote from Babylon. Each character and set of characters had a specific meaning, memorized not by the illiterate population, but by highly trained scribes, who probably went home from work after seeing little triangular shapes all day, still seeing triangular shapes. For example:

"Hi, Son. I'm home."   "Hi, Honey."

These scribes probably spent their workdays, when not actually wedging little triangles into the moist mud tablets, in searching for the mud along the banks of the Euphrates and Tigris rivers, digging it up, carrying it back to the shop on donkey's backs, and trying to get the sticky mud off feet, legs, hands and arms. (Then, of course, there was the problem of trying to find reeds of differing sizes for inscribing onto the tablets, reeds being the tools of choice.)

As these activities were time consuming, it is widely accepted and held by archeologists that no scribe ever owned a boat, although some may have been invited by friends to go for boat rides on sunny Sunday afternoons. So, we can accept that the quote was probably wedged into the mud, not by an intelligent, boating Babylonian, but by a non-scribe who had been able to pick up at least a smattering of cuneiform. Professor Strawbridge's theory is that the originator of the quote was a cuneiform school dropout, probably about third or fourth form, which others in the field believe has some merit. We can only imagine him becoming angrier at his predicament on the sandbar. Please note that near the end of the quote the inscriber has *drawn a picture of a boat with him in it, a distinct departure from the rest of the cuneiform wedges!* He probably hadn't learned the symbol for boat, shown at the end of this sentence, so simply drew the boat and sandbar, a gigantic first step forward in literary effort!

You have just witnessed the first step in what was probably the development of hieroglyphic writing, highly developed later by the Egyptians. The careful reader also observes at the end of the inscribed quote what most linguists uniformly believe to be the very first exclamation mark, emphatically inscribed, and developed to its well-known form over the past 3,000 years.

However, the biggest technological development shown in the quote is the inclusion of an at-that-time-unknown form, which we know today as a circle. It forms the underside of the punctuation mark and undoubtedly led to the birth of the wheel, tires, the dinner plate, basketballs, baseballs, and the like, children's circle games and the yo-yo, to name the most important applications of this geometrical form.

In a single quote you have now been witness to history as it occurred! And if a disgruntled boater's poking a stick into mud could be the basis for such huge leaps forward for mankind, a question naturally arises: Just what, exactly, have YOU, a person who has the advantage of modern technology, done to advance the level of human accomplishment? Huh?

You've perhaps never poked a stick or reed into thick mud. Perhaps into a playmate's eye, as a youngster. The stick thing having already been accomplished, you'll have to come up with some other means of making your mark in history. On second thought, find a stick or reed, some hard, sticky mud, and give it a try. Quite possibly, even given the advanced state of today's technological advances, you may find that the old ways are best.

YOU'VE GOT TO START SOME PLAC.

So you're a boater now. But there was a time, perhaps years ago, perhaps last month, when you weren't one, impossible as that seems to you now. For every boat you see today, whether in the water at a marina, on blocks at a dry-storage marina, in a back yard or in a driveway, or on a trailer on the highway, there was an initial reason to consider, and then buy. This was a conscious decision, made probably after a lengthy period of serious study and evaluation. Your dream boat, the boat you finally selected, fitted your particular needs, your dream boat. With tens of thousands of individually owned boats on planet Earth's waterways today, there are thousands of different reasons to take the plunge and buy, but there exists a common set of core reasons that people find appealing...

Mel Fuerster's hand reached out to quash the alarm clock's strident ring. A short search for the snooze button and...Ahh, five more minutes to get the eyelids operating. But behind closed eyelids the Fuerster brain was beginning, disjointedly, to rumble into alertness. *Monday again...already? Seems like it was just Monday yesterday...same old routine...freeze feet on the cold floor...shower...shave...cold cereal, toast, and bad coffee...disgusting commute...poor Marie...how is she able to get out of here every morning by 6:00 for six years now?...oh no, raining again...and I left the umbrella at the office...hope the boss is over his temper tantrum...his own fault, but he managed to spread the blame around...how does Marie bear up?...life's so humdrum...no ups and downs now, got to get some excitement back into our lives...how? ball club's in last place...ski?...swim?..not now in October...hiking?...wrong time of year...biking?...not the way to stay alive with all those road psychos driving who hate bicyclists... how about parachuting?...could never get Marie to jump out of an airplane...or me either.*

The snooze alarm shook him fully awake. He proceeded to go through the routine he had just visualized and headed for his car. Even here in the suburbs, 18 miles from his office in Seattle, the low roar of nearby traffic assailed his ears, as neighbors prepared, like Mel, for the agonizing, crawling, one-hour commute. But now he was alert, ready to defend himself against sleepy drivers, coffee drinking drivers, drivers still applying mascara, eyeshadow, and lip gloss, and those angry road rage filled drivers ready to shake a fist, make a gesture, honk or glower at any and all perceived driver errors, however slight.

The commute was even more agonizingly slow this Monday. *Let's see...365 days in a year, minus 104 for weekends, plus 12 for Saturday work once a month, minus 14 days for vacation, minus six days for holidays, times six years...That's over 1,500 times I've run this gamut.* He turned on the radio, hoping to find some soothing music, only to hear the commute would be further slowed by a disabled vehicle on the inside lane. Drivers were advised to find alternate routes. There were none for Mel, however, and he resigned himself to being late for work - again.

Parking was not available, all parking lots displaying their FULL signs. He finally located one several blocks from his office, and with no umbrella, suffered a wet, cold walk, made more unbearable by the insistence of every traffic light he approached to force his waiting further on each corner. The day was made longer by the stack of unfinished work from Friday, plus the chief's angry disposition remaining from earlier last week. No outside calls relieved the tedium of the day. Even the clock dawdled on the wall, seemingly mocking Mel as the hands slowed their usual pace around the numbers. He was first to leave. The wet walk to his car, the depressing thought of the commute home, usually a replay of the morning trip, did nothing to lift his spirits.

The easiest way to leave Seattle traveling east is to cross Lake Washington on one of two floating bridges, each over a mile in length. As usual, the bumper-to-bumper traffic was present, his speedometer barely registering movement. Mel had gone slightly over a quarter mile onto the bridge deck when the entire procession of cars stopped dead. He could see drivers far ahead of him out of their cars, doors open, attempting to find the cause of the stoppage, but whatever it was lay so far ahead it was impossible to determine. He turned off his engine, got out of the car, and stretched.

The lake lay gray, reflecting the dismal day, with Mt. Rainier, to the south, barely visible through the dirty-bottomed clouds. Wind, enough to cause him to button his coat, raised an occasional whitecap. He was about to re-enter the car when his attention was captured by the dramatic sight of a dozen small, white sailboats rapidly approaching a slim, red buoy that lay 150 yards off the south side of the bridge. He recognized this as a race day, as several other fleets, at spread out intervals, were following the white fleet up the lake, driven by the chilling north wind. It appeared to Mel that they were using the red buoy as a turning point during the race. The leading four boats were so close together he fully expected to see collisions as they turned and headed back down the lake again on the next leg, but they each rounded without mishap, although not without shouting from the boats' skippers that he could only dimly hear.

The last of the group rounded the buoy, and within minutes the second group of larger boats drew close. A cluster of three reached the buoy nearly simultaneously. There was not enough space for each. Mel could hear wild shouts, see frantic maneuvering. As they began sorting out tactics, he could see a man in each of two boats attaching small red flags to their backstays. While the first fleet blew down the lake like small white clouds skimming the surface, the second group, as each boat turned the buoy, exploded into veritable rainbows of colors as spinnakers popped open. Their decks were beehives of activity as the crews performed their duties to trim sails to best advantage. Then, as quietly as they had arrived, they were gone, a riot of color on a gray day. Mel's heart raced. Never had such a sight gripped him. He was riveted to the scene, with a third group approaching.

"Hey, fella, move that *&#^@# heap! The angry voice, accompanied by strident honking from the car behind, broke his reverie. He leaped into his offending car, to see that the line had moved forward only several feet. The slow pace enabled him to scan the lake elsewhere than the race course. Three small outboarders trolled

11

for fish, a large cabin cruiser moved slowly along the shoreline, and on the north side of the bridge Mel could see a number of sailboats heading nowhere in particular, zigging and zagging, simply enjoying the afternoon's brisk breezes. He imagined those sailing were much like himself. He envied them. They had broken those tightly-fashioned walls of circumstances that allow little, if any, time to do the things in life that enabled them to feel they were living their lives to the fullest. In that instant of clarity his mind was made up. There was now in his soul a void, and an ache in his heart that must be quelled. He would become a boater. But first, he would have to convince Marie that this could become a welcome break in their lives.

The vivid action at the buoy refused to leave his mind, and by this time had replaced the entire listing of possible activities he had imagined only this morning as he lay in bed. He could visualize himself, tiller in hand, maneuvering his boat in heavy winds, gaining advantage over his competitors, with Marie expertly handling the sails. The hull rising and pounding back into the cresting waves, the cold sprays of icy water splashing their faces and the shouts of other skippers became real to him. Fifteen minutes stalled on the floating bridge was about to alter his life.

December in Seattle and environs - windy, rainy, foggy, cold, flurries of snow or hail, and freezing rain that turns highways into skating rinks. But Mel was happy. Since last October's pulse-pounding scene on the bridge he had quietly made it his goal to become as knowledgeable as possible on all phases of boating, power and sail. He picked the brains of those friends he knew were boaters. He exhausted the library's boating collection, often bringing home four books at a time to study late into the night. The commute became bearable now, as he reviewed in his mind the Rules of the Road, motor operations, troubleshooting motors, sail handling, race tactics, anchoring procedure, effects of tides and currents, cruise planning, knot tying, and the myriad of things one needs to know to become a competent boater. He took a course in boating from the local Power Squadron, and would bounce out of bed Saturday mornings to visit local boat dealerships and marinas. He was hooked! Marie declined ⸱⸱⸱ invitations to go along on these occasions, preferring to sleep in ⸱ from her own workweek.

Marie's life hadn't changed yet, except she was happier now that Mel had found something to take his mind off work, the weather, the commute, and his generally ho-hum life. A major problem lurked in the back of Mel's mind, on how best to approach Marie about buying a boat. It nagged at him. She could swim, but the water was always too cold for her. She had enjoyed the few picnics they had gone on when first married, but spiders, snakes, and ants bothered her, so they had discontinued those outings. She was simply not an outdoors person; she enjoyed bridge, opera, theater, and entertaining friends. He had suggested hiking, but cougar and bear sightings reported in the newspapers frightened her. Tennis was a possibility, but long waits for court openings dulled enthusiasm. No, boating was the best answer. But how to approach her about it?

The answer occurred one evening, with Marie herself providing the opening. Mel had taken to reading Internet boating articles on the library's computer, often until the library closed. This evening he had returned home at 10:30 P.M. Marie, usually in bed when he returned, was still up, in pajamas and robe, sitting on the sofa and looking quite sullen.

"Hi, Honey. I'm home. Still up, I see."

"How clever of you to notice," she replied stonily. "Do you know what time it is?"

"10:37. Something wrong with the bedroom clock?"

"Mel, we need to talk. You've been coming home late two and three times a week since October. You hardly ever come to bed with me. And you leave and are gone most Saturdays. And you're always so...happy! " She almost spit the word.

"And you don't complain about anything any more!"

"You're right. Guess I've been caught up in a whirl lately." He sat there, watching her, wondering where this was going.

"You forgot my birthday last week! You've never missed one before, ever!"

"Marie, I'm sorry. Forgot...Make it up to you."

"You can't make up forgetting. Mel, I want the truth...Are you having an affair?"

He was stunned. Marie was a lovely woman, intelligent and fun to be with. He was an honorable man living up to his marriage

13

vows in every way. Never had he even thought about another woman. Her question was so ludicrous to him, and came so unexpectedly, that reflexively he smiled and allowed the smallest chuckle to escape his lips. His mind was vacant of any response.

She took his silence as confirmation of her suspicion. "So that's it! I've suspected for two months now that something is going on. I just hope it's not with one of our friends. And just where do I fit in to this sordid scenario?"

Mel's sense of humor and his mind returned, unfortunately in that order. "Marie, yes, I am having an affair, with a lady to be named later, but you'll always be my first mate." He smiled at his own clever retort.

"No way! You're worse than presidents are. They have their First Ladies.. and their mistresses! You're nothing but a...a...a...Don Juan! Nothing else!"

"Sweetheart, I'm so sorry. I was trying to be funny. The affair I'm having is with a boat I like. That's the unnamed lady I referred to that we'd have to name. And you don't have to be first mate. You can be captain if you like."

A long, tearful discussion followed, until Marie was satisfied her accusation was in error. Mel claimed he'd learned what he needed to know and would be home nights.

"Mel, you mentioned buying a boat. Why, after all these years, a boat?"

He described the bridge scene and action that had gripped him, explaining how it had affected him. She saw his high interest and enthusiasm.

"I don't know. I've never been on a small boat before. And sailboats...aren't they tippy? I'll bet I'd be seasick all the time. Where would you keep it? Aren't boats quite expensive? There's a lot of upkeep on a boat. If you left it at a marina there'd be monthly mooring fees. I'd have to buy just scads of new boating clothes. None of my friends have boats. How could we take time off to enjoy one?"

He could see, as she continued her seemingly unending inventory of reasons why they couldn't possibly own a boat, that the outlook appeared dim. But that comment of hers about scads of new clothes. That had possibilities for pursuing. She loved to shop for clothes. He would keep that in mind. The trap hadn't quite closed on him yet. There was hope, if only he could develop a strategy.

In January of every year, Seattle plays host to one of America's largest boat shows. The Kingdome, usual host to this magnificent event, is crowded with boats of all sizes, from canoes and inflatables that one person can carry, to huge sail and powerboats capable of circumnavigating the globe.

It is a two-week boating love-in. Everything imaginable to outfit any-size boat is available at the best prices of the year. The concourses are filled with vendors, cruise line reps, and boating-related items of all sorts. Smiling boat dealers and boat-loan-arranging bank reps lurk everywhere, ready to snare and enroll eager buyers with low down and easy monthly payments. Like bright fish lures, the boats are shined up daily, attracting buyers. Most booths show cassettes of their boats in action, always with handsome and beautiful models operating them, and always in bright sunshine, as if that were the norm in Seattle and Western Washington.

Mel sat on the sofa, Sunday paper in hand, almost inhaling a boat show special advertising supplement. His attention was fixed, not only on the next Saturday's boat show schedule of events, but on one small segment of it. He smiled. A crafty look stole onto his face.

"Oh Marie, you'll never guess who's appearing at the Kingdome next Saturday." He was sure she wasn't aware the boat show was on.

"The Kingdom? Must be major. Who? I can't imagine."

He was right. She didn't know. "Your favorite band!"

"The Round Corners? I thought they'd all be dead by now. Let me see."

He carefully folded the big ad so only the schedule showing the band's performance times could be seen. "There, Honey, and look, it's free!"

"Free! We haven't been to a concert in ages. Or anywhere else, for that matter." She was satisfied she'd gotten her zinger in. Mel winced. She hugged him.

"Hey, wait a minute! That says 1:00 P.M. Don't they give their concerts at night anymore?"

"Well, you said yourself they haven't been around for a long time. Gotta start somewhere if you're on the comeback trail. Or, maybe they're booked that evening."

"We'd better get there early to be first in line and get good seats. I'll bet the Kingdome will be packed. They were a very good band. I want to get up close. We'd better leave here about 10:30 A.M. Hope it's not raining."

Mel wasn't sure, now, that this was the good idea it had seemed when it had initially come to him as a plan to get Marie into the Kingdome and the boat show. How would she react when she found the aging band's appearance would be on a tiny stage, on the concourse level, not for a performance featuring themselves, but to provide background music for boating enthusiasts?

AT THE BOAT SHOW

"Hurry, Mel," urged Marie. They hoped to be early enough to get parking close by. "Why, there's hardly anyone here yet," was her observation as they paid and pulled in. "I remember the last time we came to their concert we had to wait in line for nearly three hours to buy tickets."

"Remember, Dear, they're older, their music is dated, and we *are* early." They walked quickly, the chill January wind nipping at their ears and noses. Mel hoped she wouldn't notice the huge boat show sign on the Dome's outer wall, and, with her head and eyes down, she didn't. There was no one in line at the ticket booth.

"Mel, why are you paying? The ad said it was free."

"Honey, you know the Dome is huge inside. There's probably another attraction booked at the same time." He had escaped for the moment, but could feel a large bead of perspiration trickling down his spine. They entered the main floor on a royal red carpet that seemed to go on forever. And boats! Crowded together, covering the entire main floor, the number exceeded even Mel's expectations. Magnificent!

"Mel, you were right. See that gigantic banner hanging there? It says BOAT SHOW. *That* was the other attraction you had to pay for. Let me see the map you picked up. I want to find where Stage C is located." He handed her the map, gazing around at the sheer magnitude of the scene. His heart was pounding with excitement.

"Marie, the crowd hasn't started to arrive yet. What say we look at some of these boats on our way to the stage? There are some real beauties here." They sauntered along the carpet, stopping now and then to admire several eye-catching models in this section of powerboats. Mel pointed out various features to a rather impatient, disinterested Marie. They neared the end of the row of boats.

"Mel! Look at this one! It's gorgeous! She ran her hands over the hull of what Mel believed to be the prettiest boat he'd ever seen. The 18-footer's shining, baby blue hull was embedded with thousands of gleaming, metallic gold flecks, sparkling under the bright spotlights playing on it. The soft seats were of a darker blue, exuding comfort underway. The general lines suggested high speed, the console, and twin 100 horsepower engines hanging on the transom reinforcing that image. "I didn't know they made such pretty boats."

"This isn't for the average pleasure boater, Marie. See those wings on each side? They're called sponsons, allowing greater boat stability at high speed. This is actually a boat designed for people interested in racing." He agreed it was a beauty, and they moved on.

Mel spotted his dreamboat, the O-28, as they neared the sailboat section. He had finally decided sailing was the way he wanted to go, recalling often the exciting scenes from the floating bridge. It seemed almost like an old friend, though he had never actually seen one before, except in ads he had read. They climbed the stairs to the deck and stepped into the cockpit. Mel gripped the tiller, waggled it a bit, and knew he had made the right choice. All the sailboats in the show had their sails up, and because of large fans blowing air on them, gave the perception of boat movement. He imagined himself racing in close quarters against the others. To him it was real. Marie had gone down the four steps into the cabin. Squeals of delight reached Mel's ears; he followed her down below.

"Mel, it's just like a big doll house down here. I can stand upright and you can too. Look at the bunk space. What a nice kitchen! So convenient to the dinette. Lots of drawer space! And look, the toilet even has a mirror and wash basin. A person could live here."

"Honey, we...that is...they, call the kitchen a galley , on boats, and the toilet is always called the head."

"Huh! The main part of the toilet is the seat. Why don't they call it the seat, instead? And look how the woodwork glistens. I love the interior layout!"

"WE CAN'T AFFORD THE DINGHY HONEY..."

"This line of boats is known for its design. This interior wood is all teak." He was highly encouraged by her reaction to the O-28. He was in his element now. He was going to live his dream. They inspected the deck areas, cockpit storage, anchor locker, sails, and finally, reluctantly, climbed down the ladder to the main floor, where Mel examined the keel and rudder. Mel introduced Marie and himself to Barney, the salesman, who, seeing their interest, gave them brochures and a basic price list. They wandered on.

"Mel, look there. It's a marine clothing store. Look at all those cute boating outfits."

Mel didn't have to be hit over the head to know an advantageous opening when one occurred. "Let's go in. I see a sweater over there you'd look good in."

"You mean the pullover with the anchors, starfish, fish, and flags? I already spotted it. Hope they have my size."

It cost more than they had expected, but he paid gladly. It was now part of his plan. He would buy even more, if she wanted, to keep her positive mood flowing. Perhaps, then, he could talk her into buying the O-28, to have a place to wear the nautical clothing she loved. Desperate thoughts in this critical situation, but he filed it away in his mind.

Stage C, up the steep stairs leading to the concourse area, was not hard to find. With a half hour to go before concert time, no eager line of fans crowded the stage entrance. Marie looked with surprise at the setup. Five microphones, tangled black cords, and 20 folding chairs were all that was there. "Mel, we're the only ones here, and it's only 30 minutes before the show starts. What's going on?"

"They'll be here. The leaderboard still says a 1:00 performance. They're already set up." They sat for a moment, resting feet weary from the unaccustomed walking.

"Mel, we have time. I've got to run to the ladies' room. On my way back I'll stop to look at some more of those darling boating outfits. Why don't you stay here and save our seats? I'll be back in time."

"Okay, don't get lost." He settled back in his chair. From where he sat above the main floor of the boat show, he could see the O-28, sails fluttering in the breeze. An intense longing assailed him, magnifying as he observed another couple in its cockpit, the man moving the tiller as Mel had done while aboard. He scanned the brochure and price list again. *I love that boat. I need that boat. Marie liked it, I could tell. It's big and comfortable enough. There're so many places to cruise around here. We can afford it...have to find a moorage...entertain friends aboard...bring a change of pace to our lives...do some racing...RACING! I could run down there right now and buy it! If Marie stops for long to look at those clothes I could be back before.....*

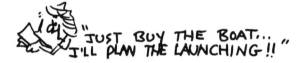
"JUST BUY THE BOAT... I'LL PLAN THE LAUNCHING!!"

A compelling force jerked him from his chair and forced his legs to march in quickstep down the stairs and to the O-28. Barney greeted him warmly, knowing, from long experience, the look on Mel's face as one ready to buy, a determined look.

"Barney, has this O-28 been sold yet?"
"That couple poking around on the foredeck just put down money on it. Afraid it's sold. They'll leave it here during the show, and pick it up later." Mel's heart sank. Shoulders sagged. He grimaced in pain.
"I see you're interested. I'm taking delivery of another O-28 here in town in two weeks. It's exactly the same boat, same equipment, same great price as this one. Only difference will be the hull color, a deep sea blue with a light blue deck and cockpit area."
Mel grabbed Barney's shoulder in his excitement. Blue! That was the color Marie seemed to like. Her various outfits had all been shades of blue. "I'll take it!" he blurted out involuntarily. "Where do I sign? How much down? Here, I'll write you a check! Just tell me how much."

Barney, awed by the rapidity of the sale, produced the necessary paperwork. Business concluded, the two shook hands, Mel still unbelieving that he had done something so brash without conferring with his wife first. The entire transaction had taken only eight minutes. Now, as he raced back to the stage, he wondered how he would break the news to Marie. Not just now, he concluded. He had two weeks to figure out a way, and he WOULD find one!

On stage, five men with scraggly beards, probably in their 50's, Mel thought, prepared for their first number. Marie had not yet returned, but as the first notes sounded she slid onto the chair next to him, more packages in hand. She'd been busy. Including themselves, Mel counted seven fans in the audience. The music might be out of date, but it was played loudly and well. And it was free!

Mel tossed and turned in bed all Saturday night, weighing the possibilities for their future, still in a high state of excitement. Sunday morning found him bubbling excitedly, pacing around the house. By noon, Marie could stand his sighing and pacing no longer.
"Mel, what's with you today? Are you okay?"
He could not help himself. The secret was too big to hold inside any longer. "Marie, Sweetheart, do you remember the O-28 from yesterday, the sailboat we spent some time on? I've got to tell you...While you went to the ladies' room and shopped...I couldn't help myself...I went downstairs...talked to Barney...and...bought it. Not the show model, but a blue hull exactly like the one we were on. I put $2,500 down, and we take delivery two Saturdays from yesterday. I just know you'll love..."

She sat down as if shot. Her hands clutched her head as she gasped several deep breaths, then laughed hysterically for several seconds. Finally, a last few gurgling chuckles escaped her lips. She looked at him, her smile growing larger.
"Mel, I've got to tell you... Yesterday, when I left you on Stage C, before I visited the ladies' room and shopped, I went back to that blue power boat. You remember the one? It had all those gold flecks...and...I bought it, along with a trailer...We'll have to have a trailer hitch welded onto my four-wheel drive to tow it."

We drop the curtain here, not because the scene gets ugly—far from it—but because it's difficult to describe two people hugging tightly and laughing uproariously. Laughing because of the capricious and unexpected twist of events that had led them from a no-boat family to a two-boat family overnight, with no idea two days ago that this could be possible.

Author's Note: True closure for the Fuerster's boat show experience could not occur for you, the reader, without my inclusion of the following news article. Clipped from the sports pages of a Seattle newspaper two years after their purchases, it is brief. I leave the minor details to you and your imagination.

Seattle: Special to USP: Marie Fuerster, by winning all three heats of yesterday's Class A limited hydroplane races on Lake Washington, clinched this year's "Hydro Boater of the Year" award. The second-year driver, also voted "Best Dressed" by her peers, performed faultlessly, her daring acts of steering around the buoys giving no opportunities to her rivals to pass, with some after-race talk from the grumbling losers to ban women from the sport. When interviewed after the races, she said her only regret was not having her husband, Mel Fuerster, present to share her success. Mel, a nationally recognized sailboat racer, is at this time in San Diego training with the Fred Furnier Syndicate as tactician and helmsman to challenge to become the American representative in the upcoming America's Cup Races.

HEAVE HO!   SHOVE OFF!

NAMING THE BOAT

There are many decisions that will affect the directions your life will take. Big decisions, relating to college, career, marriage, and children face us all. For a certain group of people, the issue of whether or not to buy a boat carries equal rank with the aforementioned problems. If the decision is made to buy a boat, a whole new set of choices is presented. Sail or power? What size? Marina moorage, dry storage or trailer? Where to go on vacations? Inflatable dinghy or traditional? How much bigger will the second boat be? You get the idea. These are *real* problems that need solutions.

However, all these decisions pale in comparison to the choice that has split couples apart and created a new field of specialization for lawyers. That is, who gets the boat? If you thought naming your children was difficult, you'll think it was child's play when you realize the difficulties of naming a boat.

"Oh Ted, it's *beautiful!*"
Deena and Ted Dobert stood on the dock, arm-in-arm, as their newly purchased sloop, a sleek, white-hulled 30-footer, was transferred from the truck to a sling and lowered into the water at the marina.
"Sweetheart, it's a new life for us now. And when we have kids, boating's a super family activity. Our sons will love it."
"And so will our daughter, Ted. Women's sailing is growing by leaps and bounds."

A dock worker, mooring line in hand, tugged the majestic sloop to dockside and cleated it down. He showed the proud owners how to start the diesel engine. The bubbling gurgle at the exhaust pipe was music to their ears. It took several minutes to motor to their assigned moorage, and they cleated down like old pros.

"Deena, what did you see on all the boats here that we don't have yet?"
"Bird droppings, but I imagine we'll have them soon enough, unless we take steps to keep the birds away. I don't want to have to

23

clean bird mess every time we take the boat out for a sail."

"Well, yes, but there's something else. We don't have a name on our boat.."

"Of course. It's brand new. But yes, we need a name. Something beautiful. It's all white. How about Ghost, or Phantom? What else is all white?"

"Typing paper and sheep fleece."

"Ted, don't joke around. Besides, what about black sheep? How about Lily or Snowball? The winds are so light around here in the summer. Maybe Puff?"

"Deena, once the name we pick is on the boat it's there to stay. And don't forget, we'll be racing once we learn more about it. I suggest a powerful name, one that suggests strength of performance, like Thunderer or Savage, Wild One, or maybe Gladiator. Seems that type of name would help psych out competitors."

"I don't know. We could combine your ideas and mine. How about White Lightning? That's powerful, and it does describe our boat's color."

"Hmmm. Not bad, but that's another term for moonshine, you know, illegal liquor. Bad for kids to grow up with that. Don't want to give 'em bad ideas."

"You're right, but those names you suggested detract from the boat's beauty. How about Aurora, or Drifter?"

"Drifter?.. Honey, no way for a racing boat."

"Racing, schmacing! We'll be cruising, too. Think, Ted. Maybe the name Drifter will cause your competitors to become overconfident. They relax, you win. I just thought of more names. Explorer, Ranger, Searcher, Prospector."

"No, more like Rogue, Sentinel, Hurricane, or Guerrilla."

"Guerrilla? No way! Sounds like a revolutionary army group. I like Saucy, Scamp, Rambler, or Adventurer."

"Try Enforcer, Rattler, Rocket, Exploder, or Battler."

"Polaris, Pearl, Scudder or Wanderer would be good."

"No, Spoiler, Predator, The Force, or Blazer fit well."

"Not as much as Misty, Peerless, Dove, or Amity."

"How about these? Tyrant, Obliterator, or Menace?"

"Pixie, Freedom, Zephyr, or Scout."

"Brave Heart, Executor, Dominator, or Conqueror."

"Windsong, Bluebell, White Mist."

"Warhoop, Villain, Rascal, Nasty."

"Nasty! Ted, this is ridiculous! Here we are, arguing over something so inconsequential that I can't even believe it. I let you talk me into buying this boat. I did it to please you, but now, after being on it and seeing the beauty of the below-deck accommodations...I really do love it. And remember, that without both our salaries we'd never have been able to afford it. Really, it's half mine."

"Okay, Deena. You want the inside or the outside? The front half or the back half? Above the waterline or below?"

"That does it! I'm serious and *you're not!* You're making fun of me. Take me home *now!* Never mind! I'll take the bus! Then I won't have to listen to any more of your idiotic boat names."

"Deena, I didn't know you were so upti...so *serious* about this boat naming business."

"Yes I am! It represents a big investment, nothing to joke about. Ted, I can see that we need professional help. Now that I've seen the real you, we need to make an appointment to see a counselor to help us resolve this power struggle."

"The *real* me? *Power struggle*? All over a boat name?"

"Ted, boats' names have always been female in nature. Think of some great ships...*Queen Mary, Queen Elizabeth, Nina, Santa Maria*...and just look there on the stern of the boat opposite us...*Ermintraut Offensprichheit.*"

"Yes, that's one pretty name, all right. How about *Titanic*? That sounds to me like where our marriage is going."

"And look farther down...*Virginia L, Mary Anne, Penelope S*...and just think of all the old-time clipper ships and sea-going vessels. What did they all have up front at the bow? Certainly not carvings of hunky men!"

"Nope. Bare-breasted women. Okay, Deena, we'd better see a counselor before things get worse."

"Good, Ted. I'll call today and make an appointment. When we get home go find your sleeping bag. Until we get this resolved you're sleeping on the couch!"

"Good morning, Mr. and Ms. Dobert. I'm Dr. Michael. To ease the situation, I suggest we go by first names. Your call to my receptionist suggested you're having naming problems that are not being easily resolved."

"Yes, Michael. My husband wants to select a name that suggests power, strength, and perhaps even cunning. Because a name is one's forever, I want one that implies beauty, peace, or harmony."

"I see. Yes, this can be a bone of contention, but I believe it's not insurmountable. Before we continue, please go relax over in the couch area...No, Ted, not on the same couch as Deena. Please use the other one for yourself. Thank you."

"Sorry, didn't see the other one. But Michael, I've always believed one's name defines his or her position in life, something to live up to. Look at some famous names in history. No wimpy names there. Certain names *command* respect. Others are ho-hum, neutral. Look at my own name. Ted...Theodore...Just think of Teddy Roosevelt and his brave charge up San Juan Hill against an entrenched enemy. And his motto, 'Speak softly, but carry a big stick.'"

"Hmm. Have you brought your lists of names with you today?" Both nodded yes and handed Michael their lists, which had grown considerably since the scene on the boat. He examined them carefully, jotting some notes for himself.

Deena was visibly agitated, and spoke as soon as Michael looked up. "But Michael, when I think of Ted it reminds me of a teddy bear, cuddly and soft, or a teddy, the intimate undergarment men give to women."

"Now wait a minute, Deena."

"Ted, I believe you both have legitimate points here. A name, as you both can now see, is open to many degrees of perception by different people. Think for a moment of the name Joseph...I see you both shrug, an apparently neutral name. Now think Joseph Haydn, the great composer. Ah, inspiring, soaring, majestic music that will be with us forever. Now think Joseph Stalin, ruthless, murdering, communist dictator. I'll bet your blood pressure just went up 20 points. Joseph DiMaggio, sports hero. Excitement, happiness, relaxation, recreation. And Joseph, husband of Mary, Mother of Jesus. Love, awe, humility, morality. You see, your perceptions are shaped by what you have learned about these people themselves. As perceptions are shaped individually, we must respect how every person's life experiences mold the thoughts that become the basis for the way he or she feels about, in your case, a name. Is that clear enough for your understanding?"

The two stole shy glances at each other and nodded yes. "I see awareness. That's a good start. If you can accept differences, you should become very much more tolerant towards each other's choices. Deena, you don't look pregnant. When is your child due? I'm glad to see you're looking so far ahead on this matter."

"Michael, I'm not pregnant. How'd you get that idea?"

"Sorry, I assumed this was a matter that had to be decided fairly soon. I suggest you two now go over the names on your lists to determine jointly which ones you can eliminate. I must admit that to me, some are highly unusual, even...far out.   But I do respect your ability to decide, based on what we've discussed this morning. But one thing I've learned about children is so true. Kids do tend to live up to strange and unusual names. As your counselor may I suggest you not even consider the name 'Nasty,' Ted. It's on your list and gave me a start when I saw it. I assume it's not for a daughter, but any boy would tend to try to live up to it by acting out in socially undesirable ways. There are several others that could cause problems, but that one should be crossed out, believe me. Now, on a clean sheet of paper make two columns, one titled boys, the other, girls."

"Michael, boys...and girls?"

"Right. Kids are born either boys or girls, as I recollect."

"Michael, I believe we have a slight mix-up here. The names we've been fighting about are not for a child. They're for a boat. He wants to race. I want to cruise."

Michael's jaw dropped in astonishment. "A boat!...Not a child!...A boat!..." He was silent for a moment.

"Deena, Ted, you're right. This is a terrible mix-up. I specialize in problems involving families with children and verging on breakup. The counselor who specializes in boating problems is just down the hall, but he's not in today. Our building receptionist must have routed your call here by mistake."

All three sat in silence for a few moments. Deep thoughts whirled in their now-confused brains.

"Ted, Deena, I think I may have helped on some important points today. Let me offer a suggestion for your naming problem to save you another counseling fee. I assume that cruising will take up most of the time you'll spend aboard. I see you both nod yes. First, Deena picks her favorite name and has it painted onto the transom."

Deena smiled as if the matter were settled. She had won!

"Michael, that's very one-sided. Hardly fair to me."

"Wait. I'm not done. After the paint dries........................ "

STOP! READ NO FURTHER! THE FOLLOWING IS A TEST THAT MAY WELL ALTER YOUR LIFE FOREVER!

If you, dear reader, were a boating/marriage counselor, what would you suggest as a solution for the common problem Ted and Deena face? If your answer shows promise, you could win an all-expenses-paid scholarship to the Happy Hills Hospital's lecture and training series for boating counselors. If successfully completed, you will be on your way to a really high paying, satisfying career in boat counseling. Be your own boss! Hire a beautiful or hunky secretary! Live in a gorgeous home on the water! Drive a new car every year! Commute to work by boat, or your own helicopter!

Instructions: In the box below, submit your solution to the problem, in 100 words or less. Use #3 pencil. No smudges.

If your solution is insightful, intelligent and practical, and is selected by the counselors at Happy Hills, expect the Scholarship Awards Committee to knock on your door soon.
Send solution to:

Scholarship Opportunities in Boat Counseling Dept.
Happy Hills Hospital and Rest Home
6 Milipon Drive
Floraton, San Grande Island, AN-36

Now, back to Michael's successful conclusion. (Do NOT send his in as your own!)

"Ted, after the paint has dried, fashion a frame of stainless steel, larger than the painted name, and bolt it onto the transom. Carve the name you want for racing onto a section of teakboard slightly smaller than the frame. When racing, slip your carved name into the frame and secure it in place. When cruising, simply remove the carved wooden name and cruise with the painted name showing. The steel frame should frame her painted name beautifully."

"Michael! Great idea! It's so simple. Why couldn't we have thought of that! I'm handy, even got a router. I'll bet it will only cost $80 or so to do the whole project."

"Ted, I'm glad. And I can see from Deena's smile that she agrees. But better make that $680 for the job. You forgot to add my fee for today's counseling. Please make out a check for $600 and leave it with my secretary on your way out."

See how easy this is? Could you do better than Michael? I could, if I could get out of this straitjacket and write something in the box. Besides, in this padded room there's not even a table to write on. Well, they've got to let me out some time. I'll enter the contest then.

AT THE MARINE HARDWARE STORE
The Sales Pro

Boating! Once you are hooked, you're HOOKED! No one can explain the urge to own a boat. It miraculously creeps, leaps, and clings to one's mind. And once the idea is burning inside you, you WILL, sooner or later, purchase a boat, meanwhile manufacturing the most logical, but sometimes outrageous, reasons for doing so. Having taken the first logical step, that is, justifying the reasons for the purchase, the next step is searching for, that followed by the actual purchase. (See related story - *At the Boat Show.) This being such an emotional time, most future boat owners do not look far past the actual purchase*, their minds beclouded by visions of not only the boat itself, but of romantic cruises to faraway places, which only .00000002% of all boat owners will actually take. Inevitably, the next step will soon follow, equipping the boat, most new owners not realizing, till too late, that the boat's purchase may not be the biggest expense.

"Hello, Sir. May I be of some help to you?"

"Why, yes, thanks. I'm Norv Cluer. I just purchased a sailboat, and I'm pretty green at sailing. Perhaps you could suggest a few things I might need, as I've not sailed her yet."

"Ahhh, a beginner, eh? We have just what you need. You'll want the basic equipment. Are you going to be racing or cruising?"

"Just cruising for now. Probably racing later, after I've learned the boat and the racing rules. I understand they can be pretty complicated."

"Let me get you a shopping cart, Mr. Cluer. Now, you'll probably want to travel a little faster than the other cruisers to get prime dock space at the end of the day, won't you?

"Why, I never thought of it that way before, but you're right. Get to the dock first! What's it going to cost?"

"Now, now, Mr. Cluer. Remember, in boating, if you have to ask the price..."

"Sure. Didn't think. Sorry 'bout that."

"That's perfectly all right. After all, you are a beginner. Here's a boom tent for keeping off sun or rain while you're at anchor. It's on sale today only, and I'll throw in these ties at no extra cost to you. Here're anchors. Can't anchor properly with rocks or bricks. Heh heh. Just one of our little in-house jokes, Mr. Cluer."

"To tell the truth, I hadn't thought about anchoring."

"Right, Mr. Cluer. May I call you Norv? That's why we professionals can suggest things to you that you'd never think about till you needed them. Ever try to buy an anchor out on the lake or sound? No way. And here, I'll put this backup anchor into the cart for you in case you lose the first one. Here's chain...I'll cut about 20' of one-inch for you. That'll keep your flukes from dragging. Must feel secure at night, right, Norv? Keep you safe and let you sleep."

"Right! Not end up on the beach or on rocks."

"And here's line. Probably 200 feet of half-inch will do. I'm sure you'll be happier with the gold line. White is so common, and the gold's only four cents a foot more. Here're shackles and pins for connecting properly. Let me call my assistant over to help load things. Charlie, could you bring over another shopping cart for Norv? Thanks. Of course your family will be aboard. Have children? Boating's great for kids. Gets 'em away from the TV set. Healthy!"

"Got a wife and three kids, ages 7, 9, and 11."

"Family safety is sooo important. Here are five flotation devices, PFDs, we call them, and the right size for everyone. I'll throw in a compass for navigational help. Let's see, you'll need a global positioning locater, depth sounder, horseshoe ring and bracket, and it always helps to know how fast you're going. I'll throw in this digital knotmeter. Tells to the closest tenth of a knot how fast you're going."

"I don't know. $850 seems a little steep just to know that."

"Norv, you can trim your sails by it. And you'll want it for racing at some future time anyway. Norv, you don't want to be the slowest boat out there, do you? What'll the kids think? They probably won't even want to race with you."

"Right again. They'd never let me hear the end of it."

"Here's a great 12' dinghy for you for under $1,000. This two-horse engine will drive it along nicely. Kids'll have a ball in it. Better get two six-gallon gas tanks and a case of oil to mix in. Charlie, two more carts here for Norv. Can't cruise or race without a mast-head wind indicator. Can you reach up there on the shelf and put it into the cart? Thanks. That's it. Oops! Almost forgot. Boom vang and the tackle for it. And fenders...here're four. Norv, are you all right? You look a little pale. Need to sit down?"

"I...I'm okay. Didn't realize there was so much more involved in outfitting a boat. Lucky I'm in good hands so I get the gear I need."

"Remember, Norv, most of this is a one-time expense. Tools! Can't use regular tools. They'll throw the compass off. This very nice bronze set will be perfect, and under $200. I'll throw in the plastic case with no charge, seeing what a good customer you are. If a spreader breaks, or your masthead light goes out, you'll need this bosun's chair and its heavy-duty lines. Here's your barometer. Must know what the weather will be bringing. Charlie, two more carts here."

"Nothing's more miserable than being wet and cold. Here, let's throw in these sets of rain gear for the family. Norv, you toss in that boat hook, and I'll add this log book and sail repair kit. Charts! How could I forget charts? We'll put these in so wherever you sail you'll be prepared and won't get lost. Look. Pago Pago, Red Sea, Yokohama Harbor, Philippine Sea, Straits of Gibraltar. All here and more. Oh, a sextant, in case your global positioner goes out. Here's the manual for it. Believe me, Norv, you'll want the top of the line on a sextant."

"Wait! I'm not sure I'll be cruising out of sight of land until later. Those can wait."

"Norv, Norv, Norv. That's what all the beginners say. Why, before you know it you'll be in Hawaii, Rio, the Panama Canal, Samoa. It's just the nature of sailors, once they get the smell of the sea in their nostrils. I've actually had former customers come back and be angry with me because I hadn't been more insistent about selling them charts they at first thought they didn't need."

"Makes sense. Put in the sextant and charts."

"Just about got 'er wrapped up. A few more items that no self respecting sailor would be without. Tide tables, signal flag set, spare water can, extra winch handle, folding bucket, bolt cutters, jiffy-reefing gear, and a kelp cutter. Charlie, three more carts here, please, for Norv. Cockpit cushions, belaying pins, bottom paint, and a gelcoat repair kit. Teak oil to keep your boat looking sharp, horn, and bell. Be sure you read up on Coast Guard requirements, Norv. Boarding ladder, hiking stick, fid...."

"Fid! Now just a minute! What's a fid?"

"Easy, Norv. It's a device for splicing lines, or fixing the ends of lines that are undoing. We call those loose ends 'cows'tails.' Don't want those. Sure sign of a beginner."

"Sorry. I guess I thought there, just for a moment, that you were trying to take advantage of me. Can't be too careful...Better safe than sorry."

"Norv, trust me. Let's ask Charlie. Charlie, if you were outfitting a boat, would you trust me to help you? See there, Norv, he nodded his head. Okay now, spare gaskets, worming line, flares, clam shovel, crab pot, six cans of bait, mop, and a Union Jack."

"Union Jack? Isn't that English?"

"Sure. If you cruise to England it's only proper marine etiquette to fly their flag. Oh, put in a flag staff, too."

"Better put that one back. I'll probably go the other direction. Put in a rising sun flag instead."

"See, Norv? What did I tell you? Not even out of the store yet and you're already thinking about your first major cruise. What about a Russian flag in case you cruise up around Vladivostok? Yes? I'll toss it in. But if you're going that far you should have a self-steering wind vane. Got one here for under $2,000. With it you can travel and get some sleep."

"All right, if that's what the other cruisers are carrying."

"Norv, you look like the type of man that puts family above all. What if you became becalmed at sea and ran out of water? Here's a solar still for under $1,500."

"What the heck! Throw it in! Whew! I think I've spent enough for one day. How much do I owe?"

"Just a moment...add this column...carry the three...that'll come to $33,752.27, tax included."

"Ulp! I thought that once I bought the boat the wind was free. That's a whole lot more than I was expecting to pay. Do you have an installment plan?"

"Of course. Remember, Norv, I'm outfitting you for life, almost. Just think of your wife at dockside, looking imploringly into your eyes and crying, 'Norv, how come all the other boats have solar stills and we don't?' Or your children badmouthing you because all your lines have cows' tails? Norv, this is simply a way of showing 'em all that you're just as good as they are!"

"That makes a lot of sense. You're right. Oh, I forgot to buy the one item I came in to get."

"And what's that, Norv?"

"The cheapest book you've got on how to sail."

"Here it is. I'll just add $12 to your total. Say, I never did find out what kind of boat you bought. I'll bet it's a beauty."

"I've got a picture of her here in my wallet. See? Isn't that the sweetest looking 15' day sailer you've ever seen? I can hardly wait to get her into the water."

There was a long, long silence. "A day sailer?...Fifteen

footer? Norv, I believe you'll have a little storage problem on board. But wait! Have I got a good deal for you! How much did you pay for her?"

"With trailer, $2,800."

"Norv, you do realize it's the normal boater's usual practice to move up to a larger boat later. All of 'em do it." He lowered his voice and looked furtively around. "Now don't tell the boss. If you were to buy all the gear you bought today in a year or two more, it would cost hundreds of dollars more , maybe thousands, with inflation as it is. You look like the type who will move up several times before you're done boating. I'll save you all those in-between moves. I'll give you $2,900 as a trade-in for your boat and trailer on a beauty that came in just yesterday. It was owned by a little old lady who only had it out sailing twice, and never in salt water. And Norv, *she never exceeded hull speed, either time out!*"

He looked Norv forcefully in the eyes. "You're already $100 ahead on the trade-in, and at least hundreds ahead on equipment if you buy today. You can't say no to a deal like this. The boat's a 44' ketch, sea-blue, with teak trim. The owner's asking $78,000 for her, but if you buy today I think I can swing the deal for $75,000. All the equipment you bought today will fit on it perfectly. Here, let's go down on the dock and take a look at her. Just follow me through this door. Step carefully, and don't hit your head."

EPILOGUE

How, you may ask, could *anyone* be as naive as Norv Cluer? The answer, of course, is the numb state of mind that most new boaters possess. And how could any honest salesman sell all that equipment for a boat he'd never seen? Well, you know the answer to that one. To ease your mind somewhat, I offer this report, brought to me by a tourist accustomed to traveling worldwide.

Just last May, tourists passing through the Panama canal on a large cruise ship noticed a small fleet of pleasure craft gathered to await their own traverse through the locks. One that caught their attention was a lovely, sea-blue, 44' ketch with shining teak trim.

Three happy children played on and fished off the foredeck. A woman was collecting the drippings from what appeared to be a solar still, while in the cockpit, on coils of line, sat a man, fid in hand, removing cows' tails.

-WHY GERTRUDE MAY HAVE TO ASK HER HUSBAND TO BUY A BOAT-

A LITTLE NOSTALGIA

So now you're a boater. You and the family made the *big* decision, and your boat's either at the marina or on a trailer. There was a time when you *weren't* a boater...hard to imagine that! Your entire life has changed...new use of time...new priorities...new friends...new lower bank balance. And a new vocabulary has entered your life. You've had to adjust your vocabulary because so many boating terms have entirely different meanings from those you grew up with. That was before boating became your longing, your hobby, your recreation, your obsession, and finally, your life. To those former friends, now landlubbers, who listen to your conversations, it's as though you are speaking a foreign language, only faintly understandable.

Do you remember when you thought:

*a thimble was a thing your wife kept losing under the sofa?
*a painter was a guy who splashed paint speckles all over the furniture and the carpet?
*a pennant was what the Yankees always won?
*a turtle was a swimming creature that scared the fish away?
*a pulpit was where the minister always stood too long on a Sunday morning?
*a sheepshank was to be avoided, like liver and tongue?
*a dumb compass was appropriately named because you could never find your way out of the woods with it?
*a range was a stove or what cowboys were at home on?
*a fly was that part of your pants that was always unexpectedly and embarrassingly open?
*fetch was what you could never train your dog to do?
*serving was the worst part of your tennis game?
*knots were what happened to muscles after exercising?
*shrouds were the final things corpses got wrapped in?
*bluff was what you did best while playing poker?
*freeboard was what your college grad thought he or she deserved between jobs?

*all hands was the way your daughter described her former boyfriend?
*the poop deck was where the cruising dog or cat visited at least twice daily?
*artificial resuscitation was something immoral boaters were always doing?
*bowline was where you went when you couldn't get a date?
*a bar was where you went after bowline?
*a schooner was what you ordered at the bar after bowline?
*heaving was what you did after drinking too many cold schooners at the bar after bowline?
*tumblehome was what you did after heaving up too many cold schooners drunk at the bar?
*a sheet was a large, white cloth that covered a mattress?
*tide was a soap you washed sheets and laundry in?
*a sheet was a rope?
*a line was a rope?
*a sheet was a line?
*a line was something you told a girl?
*a can buoy was a marine toilet?
*a nun buoy was a *really* mixed-up person?
*a red sector was a rendezvous area for the Russian navy?
*port was a wine instead of one side of your boat?
*alcohol was a liquid you drank, instead of a liquid you put into the boat's stove?
*a head was the hairy lump on top of one's neck?

THIS SECTION
CENSORED BY THE
BOATING STANDARDS COMMISSION
FOR
DECENCY AND MORAL
UPRIGHTNESS

Admit it! You've changed! Perhaps for the better, perhaps for the worse. (See section above. Whoever put *that* in deserved his comeuppance!) But you're not the same person that you were before boating entered your life. And all your former friends know it, perhaps even better than you do.

WHY LOST BOATERS NEVER
RETURN FROM THE BERMUDA TRIANGLE

THE SAILORS' KNOT

If you are going to be a truly proper boater, there are huge numbers of technical skills you must learn that you don't know now. One of these skills is *really* basic, having come to us from the time of the sailing ships, probably antedating the time of the pyramid builders. The skill? Knot tying. Sheet bend...timber hitch...half hitch...square knot...figure eight...bowline...sheep shank. Just a few examples of traditional, useful knots used today not only by boaters, but also by loggers, farmers, ranchers, even surgeons. There are specific knots for specific situations. *But,* one must study and learn them first.

"Hi, Honey, home from sailing class already?"

"Yeah. Got canceled. It was pouring rain, and the lake was absolutely flat. Not a breath of wind. Everyone was glad to leave. We'll get a makeup later."

"Rob, you're soaked. Better pop into something dry. What's that piece of rope for that you're holding?"

"Angie, it's called line, not rope, on a boat. The instructor gave each of us a piece. Our assignment is to master what he called the 'Sailors' Knot' before next Saturday's lesson. He said it's the most important knot to know, and that we should be able to tie it with our eyes shut, so that if we get caught in a storm at night we'd still be able to tie it. He called it a bowline. Looks pretty simple."

"Rob, we don't even *have* a boat. Are you planning on sailing to Samoa on one of those 14-foot day sailers you're training in? And I should think that if you did get caught in a storm at night you'd have more important things to do than stand around tying knots with your eyes shut."

"Oh, don't be funny. He just wants us to master the knot. Here, let me show you. See, you make a loop and push this end through and around this other part and pull tight. *Voila!* Hey, what happened?"

"Ha, ha, ha, ha! Rob, there's no knot there at all. You've ended up with just a straight piece of rope."

"Line, Angie. Maybe I went the wrong way. I went right loop, so I'll go left loop this time. Again...loop, end goes through, around here in back, down through this other loop and pull tight. Ah! See the knot forming? There!"

"Rob, that's nothing but a granny knot. I could tie that with my eyes shut *and* behind my back when I was just a little girl. Big deal!"

"Hmmm. You're right. It doesn't look like the bowline at sailing school. Wish I'd been a Boy Scout. Let's see. He gave us a cute little saying to help in tying it. The little rabbit comes out of its hole, goes behind the tree, then goes back down into its hole. Let's try that."

"You said the rabbit goes behind the tree. Does that mean it goes behind the tree and wets, like you do when we go camping, or does it go around behind the tree and come out on the other side?"

"You're being funny again. This is serious business. He walks, maybe hops, around in back of the tree. Let's try it again and see what happens. Think I've got it now. Nope."

"Rob, I've got it! I'll bet he meant your arm's the tree. Here, loop the line around your arm...That's it. Now, down the hole. Here, I'll pull."

"Ouch! Easy! Look, you gave me a rope burn, er, line burn. This might be it if I can get my arm out of your loop. There. Now let's pull it closed. Damn! It looks like your granny knot, but now there're two of 'em. That's not it."

"Rob, let's try going around your arm the other way. Wait a minute! You said the bunny came out of the hole first. Maybe it starts outside the hole, goes down into it, and goes around the tree root and *then* back out. Are you sure you got the bunny story straight?"

"Angie, it was a rabbit, not a bunny...Maybe I *am* confused. Let's try it your way. Hey! He didn't say anything about a tree root. Well, let's finish. Around the root...wait. We need a bigger loop. I know we end up with a loop somewhere at the end of this knot. I'll pull the end around my waist to make it bigger. You step into the smaller loop here on the floor. That's it. Now I'll steer the end around and down through this loop hanging from my arm. That could do it. Pull, but easy, this time, huh?"

The front door rattled open and banged shut. Son Tom.
"Hi, Tommy, how'd your game go? Win again?"
"Great, Dad! We won big. Hey, why are you and Mom all tied up together with that rope?"
"It's a line, not a rope, Tommy. Your father is just now learning a super knot for sailing. This is his homework."
"Tommy, can you hand me the end of the line there on the floor? I can't reach it, tied to Mom. Thanks. Now, can you bring that knot behind my back around front here where I can reach it? Do you see it?"
"Sure, Dad. HEY!" That looks like a bowline our scoutmaster showed us last meeting. He said it was the best knot to know. We're going to learn it next meeting. Wow, Dad, I didn't know you knew how to tie a bowline!"
"Son, DON'T TOUCH THAT KNOT! I need to study it, if I can get out of this tangle with Mom."
"TOMMY! UNTIE THAT KNOT! I've got to tend to our dinner before it burns up. I can't be standing around here all day tied up."
"She's right, Son. Untie us. Angie! I just got a great idea. There are only so many ends, loops, holes, trees, and directions. I'll run each set of possibilities through the computer, sort of a bowline program."
"All that for a dumb knot?"
"It's not dumb. You even heard Tommy exclaiming about it. The program should take only three to four hours to set up, and by Tuesday I should..."
"Dear, before you do that, *I've* got a great idea. Call your friend Harry. He's had a boat for years. I'll bet he can tell you over the phone how to do it."
"Yeah. That's a good idea. I'll call now. Hope he's home."
Harry was home, answering the phone himself.
"Harry, this is Rob. I need some help on tying a bowline for sailing class. Can you give me some tips?...Great!...Yes, I've got pencil and paper with me. Go ahead...right...up...did you say around?....And then down and through. Okay, let's see if I got it.

Make an overhand bight, then run the fall through it. Run the fall right to left around the standing line, then back through the bight, which now becomes the stirrup. Then cinch it up. Got it! Harry, anything about a bunny or a tree in there? No? Well, thanks a lot, Harry." Rob hung up and slumped in the chair.

"See? I knew Harry could help."

"Angie, read these directions."

"Okay. Mmmm. What's this mean? What's a bight?"

"Honey, I'll tell you the truth. I haven't the slightest clue."

"Why didn't you tell Harry you didn't understand?"

"And let him think I didn't know *anything?* I do have *some* pride, you know. It's sure taken a beating today, though."

"Maybe so, but you still can't tie a bowline. Ah, men! Too proud to ask for directions! Remember when we got lost last summer on our trip and ended up 75 miles from where we were supposed to be because you wouldn't ask for...." But the thought was wasted, on Rob's quick retreat upstairs to the computer station.

"Angie! I've done it! The computer says there are only 842 possible combinations to try. Even if I took one minute with each trial I'd be able to finish before Saturday's lesson."

"Rob, I think this knot thing is getting completely out of hand. Call Harry again and explain you're still having problems. Ask if you can come over and have him show you the knot personally."

"You're right. Pride be damned! I'll call now."

"Hi, Harry. Thanks for letting me come over. Shouldn't take long, with a pro like you for a teacher."

"No problem, Rob. I remember when I started boating I had to have some help, too. I'm glad to see you learning the bowline. Good knot. I've got 'em all over the boat, but haven't tried one for some time now. Here, let me have that piece of rope you brought along."

"Harry, it's line, not rope, on a boat."

"Oh...ahem...line...of course. Now watch carefully. I'll do it three or four times, then you do it. Make your bight, or loop. Then swing the end down through...."

"Harry, our instructor had us come *up* through the bunny hole, not down, like you did."

"There are different ways to make it. I'll wager I was tying knots when he was still in diapers. So. Down the hole, around the back, and...wait a minute...let me think about this...here, let's go around this other way, now down and cinch tight. Wha...?"

"Harry, you've made a granny knot. Angie's been able to tie that since she was a little girl. And behind her back, yet!"

"Let's try that again. I'll be the bunny. We'll start this time by going around the corner...."

"Harry, there's no corner in this knot. Just line, tree, and hole. Angie put in a tree root, but that didn't work either."

"Rob, I think I've got it this time. Cinch up and...DAMN!"

"Harry, there's no knot there at all!"

Time passes. It's now past midnight....

"Harry, I'm going to bed. What's going on? You've been down there over three hours now. Rob still there?"

"Nothing, Gretel. Just some minor technical difficulties. Can't seem to remember how to tie a bowline for Rob."

"Hah! Just exactly like the time you tried to show Larry Mintow how to tie a Windsor knot in his necktie. You haven't been able to tie your own tie now for years. Better come to bed. Maybe you'll dream how to do it."

"She's right, Rob. Embarrassing! Sorry. Try the library after work Monday. Look it up and practice tying it according to the picture in the encyclopedia. Let me know how you do. I'll come over to your place for a refresher."

"Good idea. Thanks for the tip. G'night."

"Hi, Angie. Back from the library with the line, and look!"

"WITH A BOWLINE IN IT! That *is* one, I presume."

"Yes, and you know, almost everyone in my sailing class was there. They all had trouble. That's one tough knot. We won't have any more trouble with it now."

"Yes, Dear. Too bad I won't see it again. That little bunny was *so* cute!"

LEIF ERICSSON DISCOFFERS AMERICA

Editor's Note: These excerpts are from the partially translated sagas of the original Olde Norske language. Archeologists located the sagas in a rock cairn on the remote island of Lefsalut, the most southwesterly island of Norway, commonly believed to be the last sight of land seen by the Viking raiders as they departed on voyages of discovery and conquest. Because the dialogue portions of this chapter are written in the original Viking tongue, readers who have difficulties comprehending foreign languages, whom we shall call language disabled, are strongly advised to skip this chapter and go on to the next. Some of you braver readers, however, may take this as a challenge and try anyway. Lots of luck! Others may wish to enroll in a foreign language class specializing in Olde Norske, learn the language, and return to this chapter at a later time.

"Leif, vy you alvays valking oop und down de house? Are proplems you haffing?"

"Borghilde, Ay tall you de trooth. It ben for veeks Ay haffn't ben on raid. Ay tink lack uf excitements gatting to me. Ay needs action."

"Vell, vy not you go down to bar tonight und pick fight vit Borge, Sven, Odmark, any uf dose tough guys. Maybe all at vunce. Den you can sit qvietly in chair to recoffer from cuts und bruises vidout all dis upping und downing, backing und forthing around house."

"Goot idee, bot you forgot Ay had big fight vit polar bear last veek. Ay'm still sore from dat, so needs qvieter someting to do. Ay haff it! How 'bout if Ay inwite six or eight uf de guys offer for big card game? Ve'f still got enuff fermented mead left ofer from de last Irish raid, und you could stir op 50 pounds or so uf lutefisk for da guys."

"No vay, Leif! Last time dat bunch of hooligans tore op de liffing room ven Torsten pulled dat hidden ace out uf sleeve to beat Lars, who already four aces. Vot a mess! Ay don' vant dem roughhousers here again, except mebbe alone."

"Yah shoor. You right. Tink Ay'll go ofer to Torsten's to see if he can host game."

"Helga, Leif Ericsson's here und vants to know if Ay can haff guys ofer for card game Saturday night. Okay vid you?"

"Torsten, don' you remember vot hoppened last time ven dat Leif Ericsson got too much gooseberry punch in him? By Odin, he vas first vun here to arrife und remember dat huge plateful uf lutefisk-on-a-stick treats Ay made? He ate dem all before anyvun else efen arrifed! Vy not you un Leif go to Ole's house to see if Astrid vill permit? Bot Ay doubt it."

Editor's Note: The next two pages of the saga were watersoaked, and over the centuries had faded to the point where they were undecipherable. When we reach the next legible page, we find there's no home willing to accept this robust bunch. Even the barkeeper at the pub won't let them into the card room, after extensive damage done to furniture, windows and the bar itself, after their last game. As we resume we find Leif, Odmark, Torsten, Ole, Sonde, Tormas, Borge, Tonder, Troms, and Sven sitting dejectedly on benches at the waterfront park overlooking the boat moorage site.

"Poys, efen de park superintendent von't lat us play gambling cards in de park. Bot, Ay go good idee. My boat's biggest vun. Lat's go aboard und sail out into bay und play."

"Yah, Leif, good idee," exclaimed Troms, 'bot Gambling Commission passed law last veek to prewent gambling vit'in two miles uf shore."

"Dot's hokay. Ve'll go t'ree miles out. You all vant to play game tonight und haff fun?"

"Yah shoor! You da man, Leif!" The response was loud and enthusiastic. They moved quickly to Leif's boat, hoisted sail, raised anchor, and headed out of the protected fjord, coming into increasingly heavy winds. By the time they were past the two-mile limit, the northeaster was ripping tops off the cresting whitecaps. The men gripped the lifelines and hoped the sails wouldn't tear, themselves becoming most thoroughly soaked by constant sprays of icy sea water.

"Leif, mebbe not too smart to play tonight. Cards von't stay on table. Mebbe turn back und play 'nother time."

"Tonder, Ay agree vit you. Let's douse sail und row back. Sven, vould you open our locker und hand effrevun an oar? VAIT!

By Odin, Ay ferget Ay took all oars to Bjarne's vood shop to gat new grips on dem. Ve'll haff to yoost poot op small sail to gat back to home."

The longboat pitched, bucked, and yawed as the waves grew higher. A snapping CRACK! sounded at the stern.

"Leif, da rodder has tore off. Vot ve do now? No vay left to steer boat!"

"Poys, notting to do bot hang on und pray to Odin de storm gos avay. Too bad, becuss Ay felt lucky for cards today."

The game, then, had become not cards, but survival. The wild storm lasted four more days. There is no record here of the thirst, hunger, and dismay of not being able to control their own destinies. The boat was driven in a southwesterly direction. On the fifth day, in easing winds, the boat was driven onto a sandy beach in a strange, unknown land thick with tall trees and vegetation.

"Leif, vare are ve? Any idees?"

"By Odin, eff somvun had inwented compass ve could tell, from direction ve came und vere blew to. Looks like nice place. No snow und ice. Look. Apples growing on trees ofer dere, und grapes ofer dere. Und wenison for dinner tonight! Look! Dere's deer! Und look dere. Efen a velcome committee coming from voods to greet us.. Troms und Tonder, you come vid me to go meet dem. Dey don' look Norske, so ve haff to use sign language, mos' likely. Talk vid peaceful woice, und smile a lot, bot keep vun hand on da battle axe, cos Ay see dey haff got bows und arrows, und dey don' look too friendly."

The two parties neared and stopped. The Vikings were dressed in animal furs and wore horned helmets. The locals, clad only in bark loincloths, wore a variety of colors painted on legs, bodies and faces. Their leader wore a bonnet of bird feathers reaching nearly to his waist. All stood uncertainly, eyeing each other.

"Poys, somvun's got to break de ice. Hallo, dere. Ay'm Leif, from somvere else. Dese poys vid me are Troms und Tonder. Ve got broken boat. Fix und go avay. Okay, guys?"

There was no response from the "welcoming committee." They were trying to determine whether the Vikings were gods, animals, or humans. The staring match continued. The locals were perplexed, but at a staccato command from their leader, a shower of arrows filled the air, causing the Vikings to fall back. Troms, stumbling and falling, was quickly surrounded by eight of the attackers. A sharp cry of pain, a yell from Leif, and the other Vikings, weapons in hand and howling like banshees, charged the new enemy, all of whom broke and fled into the dark forest.

"Troms, vot's hoppened to your head?"

Troms arose groggily, his head covered with blood. "It's hokay, Leif. Dese are pretty nice guys ve met. Dey saw dat Ay needed haircut, so dey gafe me vun. Pretty rough, though. Too bad dey run off before Ay could pay dem for it."

"But Troms, dey took off too much abofe de ears. Efen scalp is gone. On vay back to boat ve catch rabbit, skin it, und cut to fit bare spot on your head. Mebbe dat hare piece vill grow on you. Ven ve gat back home you can become barber und start 'Hare Club for Wiking Men.' You really a shore guy anyvay, alvays seasick ven vind rocks de boat. Ve guys haff to change to shorter hair. Ay'm still burned op 'bout dat Roman guy on street who saw me from behind and yelled 'Hey, Cutie, votcha doin' tonight?' He vas tinking Ay vas blonde voman."

The next few days saw the men felling trees for the rudder and the missing oars, always watchful for surprise raids from the local guerrilla forces, obviously unhappy with the Viking's presence. The work progressed slowly, hand axes and battle axes being the only tools available.

"Poys, ve almos' done," remarked Leif towards the end of the work. "Too bad no vun's inwented de chainsaw. Eff ve had chainsaw, vid all dese trees handy, ve could conquer de whole vorld! Bot for now, good to be gatting home. Ay'm tired uf eating wenison, apples, und grapes. Too bad dere's not a store around here ve could raid and gat milk, cold cereal, pork chops, pie, lettuce, und so on. Ay efen miss my Borghilde's oatmeal moosh effrey day for breakfast."

The other men chimed in. "Und lefsa!" "Und lutefisk!" "Und sqvirrel!" The list went on and on, until the men had exhausted the list of foods they missed at home. They ate more apples and grapes.

The long-awaited-for day arrived. "Leif, ve raddy to go now. Rudder und oars all done. Bot ve haff vun more important piece of bisness before leaffing here."

"Vot's dot, Ole? Ay can' tink uf a ting."

"Vy ve come here in first place? To play cards, bot novun's got cards, so vait on return to play. So, mos' important ting is...name dis place. Ay don' tink, an' Ay don' tink any uf us here tink, dat dis place has effer been discoffered before. Ve should poot it on our charts. Ay've ben talking to de poys, und ve all agree, you bein' leader, dat ve should name it 'Leifland' in honor uf you un all you'f done to keep us alife on dis adwenture."

"Ahhhh! Poys, Ay appreciates you tinking uf me, bot Ay don' vant my name associated vid dis place. Dese neighbors is awful! Raids at night, arrow showers by day, und bad haircuts alvays vanting to giff to us. Efen my vife does better job on hair den dey do."

"You right, Leif. Dis bad place. Only dose Scots vorse dan dese guys are! Vot a handful!"

"Ole, don' remind me uf dem Scots. Dot's de only time ve'fe had to take captured prisoners back vere ve got 'em."

"Vell, Leif, ef you only listened to me, or any uf de odder poys, you'd haff seen dey vas growing viskers. Und do you remember how hard dey fought?"

"Yah shoor, Ole, bot Ay had lots uf details to look after. All Ay noticed vas dat dey vas vearing skirts, und who vears skirts? Vimmens, dot's who! Ay t'ot dey'd make good vifes for de bachelors at home. Und all dat 'Hoot mon' stuff und de foreign accents dat all de vimmens fell for, hook, line, und sinker. Vot a time dot vas!"

"Und don' forget de fuss dey poot op ven ve loaded dem op to take dem back to vere ve got 'em. Dey vanted all uf our vimmens, dose bad guys!" Ole shook his head sadly.

"Und Leif," put in Borge, "remember dot vot dey called moosic? By Odin, vot a racket! Ven dey'd sqveeze dose sheep bladders, or vatefer, Ay'd haff to plug my ears or go op into de hills to gat avay. Only good ting vas ven dey vas playing, dere vasn't vun fly or mosqvito around novere. Dey vas all driven op into de hills too."

"Enough rememberin', poys. Back to naming dis place. You all remember ven ve sacked Rome, und dot Roman guy, Amerigo Vespukee, brought us vot he called beero und vino. Und ve valked crooked und fonny, und lost our way back to da boats und slept in gutter. Next day my head hurt vurse dan ven dat Czar Petrosky hit me on the head ven ve sacked Vorograd, und he finally surrendered und knighted me. Vell, Ay say it time to get efen vid dot Roman guy! Ay say ve name dis place Vespukee. Den, ef by some miracle anyvun else effer come here, dey vill associate dis horrible place vid him, und not vit me or eny odder Norske guy."

"Bot Leif, dot name sounds too moch lak vot ve vere doin' all night after drinking all dat beero und vino."

"Tonder, you right. How 'bout Amerigo?"

"Bot Leif. Ef ve do dat on charts, effrvun tink dat a Roman guy discoffered it."

"Sven, you right. Let's make small change. How 'bout America, instead?"

CASE STUDY #1
IMPROVING ANCHOR TECHNIQUE

The following case study is presented to emphasize that correct anchoring procedures *must* be followed. A beginning boater tends to ignore small details in the heady rush of buying the dream boat and its equipment, locating moorage, or learning boat trailer operation, engine operation, and other significant matters, all the while driving his or her non-boating friends crazy with boat talk. New boaters have even been known to depart on maiden voyages *without* anchor, line, and chain. Others have been outfitted properly, but on anchoring for the first time, have forgotten to secure the free end of the line to a boat cleat, resulting in anchor, chain, and line finding a permanent home alongside old tires, beer cans, crabs, clams, and other long-lost anchors in the mud of whatever waters they tried to anchor in. It must be said, in fairness to boaters in general, but beginners in particular, that anchoring is generally acknowledged to be a traumatic event. Errors made here are seldom repeated.

Case #1 - Oliver S., with sailboat racing experience, but none anchoring, his friends' boats always returning to their docks after completion of their races. His maiden voyage, with good friend Maureen T. as crew, was an exhilarating sail to Fish Bay, some 15 miles upsound from town. His new 29-footer, *Tern*, handled the breezes beautifully, and both he and Maureen were filled with the joy of life. Upon arriving, Oliver selected a scenic anchorage site some 100 yards from the beach. He made certain the free (bitter) end of the line was secured to the forward starboard cleat, checked the shackle pin to ensure that line and chain and chain and anchor were securely fastened together, and dropped anchor. The line slipped through his hands until he felt it go slack. He was on the bottom for the first time! He noted Maureen was filled with admiration at his boat handling and anchoring technique, and hoped this foretold a very cozy evening aboard, at a later time, after returning from dinner.

They both watched to make certain the boat was not dragging anchor, checking boat position in relation to points on the beach.

Satisfied, they clambered into the dinghy and rowed ashore, beaching the dinghy a good six feet from the water. The two, hand-in-hand, headed for the *Le Petite Cuisine,* an intimate French restaurant, a familiar destination for many boaters from Seattle. As mutual friends happened to also be there when they arrived, Oliver's planned two-hour dinner stretched to four hours, with good food, drinks, and conversation the order of the evening.

The Phoenicians knew, the Vikings knew, and old salts from time immemorial knew that a rising tide lifts all boats, an idea that had unfortunately escaped Oliver's boating experience. Upon returning to the beach after dinner, they discovered no beach, but a broad expanse of water, which, as they watched with dismay, was lapping landward higher each minute. White specks of sea foam led the unrelenting advance of a flood tide. The dinghy, not having been secured, had drifted away and was nowhere in sight. Oliver, after knocking on several doors, found a young lad who agreed to row them to *Tern,* a tidy profit for the young man, agreed upon and paid before their departure from shore.

As they neared the craft they could see, even with their limited experience, that all was not well. Oliver had anchored in 14 feet of water at low tide. His anchor, chain, and line totalled 16 feet. He had even measured to make sure it would reach bottom! The tide table, had Oliver one with him on the trip, would have showed a 10' rise in water depth. Nor had he given a single thought to the inexorable gravitational forces of sun and moon. If you have ever been amused at the sight of a duck's aft end hoisted skyward as it's head end searches for a meal on a lake's shallow bottom, you have an idea of the sight that greeted Oliver and Maureen, to say nothing of the young rower, trying valiantly to prevent an interior eruption of merriment from escaping his mouth.

The anchor itself had apparently become fouled among several of the sunken logs and rocks that sprinkle Fish Bay's bottom. They held the anchor in a death grip, defying the forces of sun, moon, and water. The strong, new line was also playing its role, unfortunately, with the dire result that *Tern's* stern end, rudder, and propeller hung ominously out of the water, like the duck's rear end. At the same time, the bow's first four or five feet were now only memories in the black water. They sat stunned, trying to think.

They were relieved of any solution by the starboard cleat, the weakest point in the whole scenario, ripping off the boat with a loud crack. The *Tern*, following another of nature's other unfathomable laws, crashed back into its natural element and bobbed crazily for a few moments. Upon boarding, Oliver found no further damage, but was forced to cut the anchor line to free the boat. It was a quiet trip back to Seattle. Maureen became unimpressed, failed to return calls, and clearly, Oliver believed, told all her friends, as he has been unable to get a date since.

It is fortunate that lessons can be learned from stupidity or misfortune. Oliver learned, for example, that fiberglass repair is *very* costly. He learned he is far ahead financially by not having to spend large amounts of money each week trying to impress dates, which he now can't get. This case leads quite naturally to other, significant questions, some of them rhetorical, some demanding answers, and others that probe the very existence of human nature:

*What would have been the outcome had this taken place on a lake, instead of on a large body of tidal water?
*What might have been the outcome had Oliver paid out another 60' or so of line?
*If the dinghy had capsized as *Tern* righted herself, and Oliver had rescued Maureen, would her feelings towards him have been the same as actually occurred?
*How long will it take Oliver to get up enough courage to anchor again?
*Without being able to trail my boat there, how could I get it to some other place in the universe, providing there was water? And breathable atmosphere? And fast food?
*Why are nature's laws stronger than those of mankind?
*How does gravity work?
*What is the meaning of life?

*Now that Oliver is out of the picture, what *is* Maureen's
telephone number?
*Even if I *could* get her number, if I called, do you think she'd
go out with me if she knew I owned a boat?
*Should I sell the boat and *then* call her?

THE ANCHOR: FRIEND OR FOE?

Editor's Note: The following letter was received from Dr. Siegfried Brainerde, world renowned psychiatrist. I have included it for the protection of readers of all ages.

Dear Editor: Shortly after completing this chapter on anchors, the author was ordered committed by me to the Happy Hills Hospital and Rest Home for treatment of a newly recognized mental disorder, *Anchorophobia,* a severe persecution complex. He suffered it after his mind snapped when his worst boating nightmare, a dragging anchor, actually occurred. He had anchored near Port Angeles, but awoke the following morning to find himself near Port Townsend, some 22 miles to the east of his original anchoring site. He wrote this chapter to prove his uncommonly held theory that anchors are actually *alien beings in disguise.*

After in-depth testing and evaluation, I can assure you that he's either onto something REALLY BIG, or is as nutty as a fruitcake. I rather suspect the latter, but IF there is even the remote possibility his theory is correct, and he *does* provide *very* plausible and interesting arguments, I must insist that the following warning be included as a preface to this chapter, as a warning for your readers' sakes. In the name of science, Dr. B.

WARNING! - READING THIS CHAPTER MAY BE HAZARDOUS TO YOUR MENTAL HEALTH!

Under NO circumstances should you read it if ANY of the following conditions apply to you, anyone in your immediate or extended family, or friends who may borrow the book:

1. You have a personal or family history of heart attack, stroke, cardiac disorder, high blood pressure, low blood pressure, blood pressure, or ANY deviation from what is usually considered as "normal" brain function.

2. You are presently under a doctor's care for ANY life-threatening condition, or are taking medicinal or recreational drugs of any sort whatsoever.

3. You are a smoker.

4. You are suffering from delirium tremens.

5. You are a hyperventilator.

6. You are easily frightened by aliens, UFOs, ghosts, spirits, demons, or the unknown.

7. You are a nonsmoker.

If one or more of the above apply to you, STOP!...So, you've decided to read this chapter after all. The author, editor, and publisher insist that you sign the disclaimer before continuing, absolving them from any and all dire consequences that may result from your reading this chapter.

Directions: Fill in name, age and today's date on first line. Then, put an X on the line below that you feel BEST represents your present condition. ONE X ONLY! If you mark anything other than the second choice, SKIP THIS CHAPTER!

I,_____

    Print Name   Write Name   Age   Date

being of:

___Sound mind and body, I truly believe

___Sound mind and body. I'll get a doctor's note for proof

___Mostly sound mind, but I do have my down days, and I get sore knees and ankles while jogging

___Some people think I'm crazy; they're just out to get me!

___I'm going to read this chapter! I bought this book, and it's mine! Nothing Dr. B. warns me of will stop me! And if you try to stop me, I'll get you! Watch out!

___If these aliens who've captured me would relax a moment so I could escape from their UFO, which I now call an FO, I'd check the second choice listed. Help!

Cut out the disclaimer and forward it to me at:

Anchorophobia Foundation
c/o Happy Hills hospital and Rest Home
6 Milipon Drive
Floraton, San Grande Island, AN - 36

Because the request for government funding for research to prevent and cure this serious disorder has been denied, a public research fund is being established. Please send donations of any amount you can afford. Cash only, in small, unmarked bills. Boaters everywhere will bless you.

Sincerely yours in Science,

Dr. B., Ph. D., M.A., D.T., T.D., A.B., etc.

Look...There it rests so innocently on the shelf at the boat chandlery. $42.99. Long ago "invented" to keep ships secure at anchor. Shank, eye, flukes, points, all there. We see the promotional blurb that vaunts its alleged holding power, the ad on the label showing it deeply embedded in sand, mud, rocks, securely holding a large boat in the teeth of a gale. Even their names are designed to lull unsuspecting boaters. Security Anchor...The Mole...MindEaze Anchor. But we know the lies, don't we? The lies manufactured by the advertising departments of "Anchor manufacturing companies" and their shifty-eyed salesmen. Yes, we know. You think I lie to you? The anchor! Boating's most fiendish invention!

In reality, invented by a coalition of pill makers and psychiatrists. Pills to put you asleep at night as you toss aimlessly and sleeplessly in your bunk, worrying about not if, but when, during the night your anchor will pull free. Pills to keep you awake the next day because you slept so fitfully last night. Psychiatrists, who rub their palms greedily as you relate nightmare tales on their couches. And of what? Anchors devilishly plotting to disengage themselves at night, casting you adrift to crash onto rocky shores, your death causing no anguish or remorse in their warped minds.

Yes, we boaters know. And how? By instinct, the unerring instinct of the true boater, and by deductive reasoning. You've anchored by scores of other boats in your cruising life. As you talk with their owners you find they are bankers, teachers, musicians, engineers, businessmen of every sort, and people from every walk of life. Now THINK! Have you EVER anchored by a boat whose owner admitted to being an anchor manufacturer? No, you have NOT! Or anyone even remotely connected to anchors? Again, NO!

Proof extraordinaire! If they do exist, they must go on vacation to hike, to swim, to golf, but never, obviously, to boat...or anchor.

More proof? Very well. Anchors, by their nature, are ignored totally except while in the act of being anchored. Have you ever looked at your anchor by day, except while preparing to plunge it deeply into the chillingly cold water? A recent survey taken in Seattle recently showed that only .0006% of all boat owners ever talk to or smile at their anchors. Isolated in a dark, damp anchor locker with only a moldy anchor line and rusting chain for company, they tend to grow resentful. So what do they do? They begin to rust to show their contempt and disdain for you. We know this is true, because the tags that adorn them when you buy them clearly state that they are RUSTPROOF!

And you know they lose things, on *purpose!* You know it's them, because YOU, the neat, shipshape boater, always keep things in order and in place. How many shackle pins have you lost lately? Plenty! I can hear you from here, shouting in agreement. But...was it YOU who lost those pins? They were there the last time you stowed the anchor away. We can validly conclude, then, that the anchor, in its neurotic urge to revenge against you, has unscrewed the pin and somehow, probably while your senses are overcome by engine sounds, winches grinding or sails thundering across the foredeck, rolls it unheeded into the bilge. Proof? Have you checked your bilges lately...or ever? No? Drop whatever you're doing and drive down to your marina. Yes! Now! TONIGHT! NO EXCUSES! Check the bilges and anchor locker floor.

There is no doubt that you'll find not one, but several shackle pins in the deepest and most remote sections of those places. Step quietly upon the dock, and again while boarding your boat. When the wind has quieted, and even the tiniest wavelets have stilled their slapping against the hull, you'll hear the occasional sound of a shackle pin dropping and rolling into the bilge of a nearby boat, if not your own. Further proof of the anchors' treachery!

This alien intelligence, seeking to humiliate you further, has other, even more-subtle wiles. Remember how, the last time you hauled anchor from the bottom to your deck, you were cleaning mud and seaweed off its flukes and the stock inexplicably flipped, pinching one or more fingers? Yes, it's out to *get* you! You can tell by the sullen gleam of its flukes. And what other gear you own gets into the stickiest mud possible and then defies you to clean it off? None!

You still can't believe an anchor has a mind of its own! You're hard to convince! But listen. How about the single-minded anchor that creeps about on the bottom and wraps itself around the largest rocks and sunken logs? HA! You'd forgotten about the time you spent two hours trying to release your anchor from something on the bottom. Then, after that frustration, having to cut the anchor line or be anchored to that site forever. Or how about the anchor lying peacefully atop a neatly coiled pile of anchor line? You had gone back to the cockpit for only an instant, and when you returned to begin anchoring what did you find? An erratically piled spaghetti MESS of tangled line! And who was there on the foredeck besides you? Now you're coming around, I can tell. Yes, the anchor.

Or, in a crowded moorage area, have you ever experienced the monumental crossover of anchor lines that required half a morning to disentangle? Don't lie. Yes, you have! All this time you thought it was caused by the current and wind turning the boats around each other. See the truth of what I say? But you don't have to believe me. You can prove this to yourself. The next time you're in a crowded anchorage, after the family has snugged down for the night and other boaters in the area have finished their noisy carousing, try this easy experiment: Creep slowly and quietly to your foredeck on hands and knees. Let your eyes become adjusted to the area of darkness where several lines dip into the water, and wait...and wait. Don't move, not even one small muscle. Breathe shallowly, just enough to stay alive...and watch .

After about an hour, when the anchors think all humans are asleep, you'll begin to see the lines moving, indicating a slow, insidi-ous movement of the anchors below. (For those of you who say this movement is due to tidal or current action, try this experiment on a lake. The same phenomena you are observing here will occur.) Any movement on your part at this point will stop them for perhaps another hour, perhaps the entire night, if they suspect you are tracking them. Don't move now, no matter how excited you become.

Because any diving to the bottom to observe their movement will cause it to cease immediately, skilled anchor observers are uncertain whether this represents anchor recreation, whether there is an anchor breeding or ritual "dance" involved, or whether it is merely another way for these strange beings to frustrate anchored boaters. (Very little, nay, *nothing* is currently known about the breeding habits of anchors, primarily due to the murkiness of the waters in which this takes place, and the fact that even scientists studying this movement have not been able to agree on common sets of theories as to its origin.)

Large numbers of anchors lying on lake, river, and bay bottoms suggest the breeding theory, as very few boaters report missing anchors. At any rate, it *is* known that on rainy or foggy nights they have been known to creep ashore, inexorably dragging their boats behind them, while they lie contentedly on the beach. Has this been a prearranged rendezvous to make contact with and report on progress to an alien mother ship? We can only conjecture. The large numbers of anchors from old-time schooners, barks, brigantines, galleys, dhows, and junks found on beaches would support this theory.

There it is. All there. The anchor IS the foe. Another theory commonly proposed goes so far as to claim that intelligent alien life forms, coming from outside our solar system, have landed here on Earth and taken anchor shape to be close to Earth's most intelligent life forms...boaters! This theory also suggests a gradual alienation between the two life forms, for reasons stated heretofore. It predicts a final revolution and an attempt to conquer, enslave, or possibly destroy the human population of our planet. The reasoning is quite clear. Few, if any, of our solar system's planets have the amount of water that is needed by anchors to survive in present form. Thus, their focus on Planet Earth.

Do not tell nonreaders of this book about this threat. It would only serve to needlessly frighten the general population at this point, leading to the panicked hoarding of food, and riots in the streets as people of all nations beseech their governments to take action against this catastrophic danger. Wannabe boaters will believe it is just another ploy to keep the waters as free as possible of new boaters. But remember...the anchors are listening. We must not let them know what we suspect. Their reactions might be too violent for us to defend against.

To: All loyal boaters of planet Earth and readers of this book
From : Your government, Anchor Defense Headquarters

Regardless of what many citizens believe, your government is taking the stance that the possible threat posed by theorists regarding subversive anchor activity and its potential danger to the civilian population must be taken seriously. Take these steps: When finished with this chapter, carefully burn it or cut it into such tiny pieces that even the most quick-witted and intelligent anchor forms cannot reconstruct it. Do NOT leave this book aboard your boat. Do NOT change your existing rapport with your anchor. If you do, it will know that we know that it knows that we know. The possible consequences are too horrible to contemplate. Rest assured that plans are now being formulated to ease and then eliminate this threat to our existence.

By order of Admiral Arthur Stimnet
Commander, Earth Defense System
Anchor Division

"HONEY... ANOTHER ANCHOR RAN AWAY..."

FREQUENTLY ASKED QUESTIONS
FOR
MR. BOAT PERSON

Mr. Boat Person, as a beginning boater, what steps should I take to ensure I don't *look* like a beginning boater, thereby avoiding the ridicule and embarrassment that often occurs among beginners when they find themselves around the "old salts" who are always present on the docks at a marina almost any time of the day?

Answer: I'm glad you mentioned the word "steps." Docks and ramps can become slippery. By following my instructions you'll be able to walk a dock or ramp *anywhere in the world,* with the confidence you're doing it so well that all others, boaters, non-boaters and pretty girls you're trying to impress will say, "Now *there's* a boater!" My instructions are for right-handers. I've never met any *left*-handers who boated, but should there be one reading these directions, simply reverse the handedness described. If this proves too difficult for you, take up golf, as manufacturers are slowly gaining the idea that there could be such a thing as a *left*-handed golfer by making left-handed golf clubs. DO NOT PERFORM THESE STEPS OUT OF THE ORDER SHOWN!

1. Stand in a normal position, weight evenly balanced on both feet. Make certain both feet are pointing in the same direction and straight ahead, not at some angle you don't wish to go. Knees should be firm, not locked, and pointing in the same direction as the feet. Arms should hang loosely at sides with palms pointing towards the legs. Chin is up, but not more than three inches from the chest, and head centered above the neck, not canted severely towards one side or the other. A confident smile will complete the picture of a knowledgeable boater about to embark on a journey, even though it may be only to your boat to remove garbage you forgot last weekend.

A word here to the corpulently challenged. So that you will be successful in dock-stepping, a severe sucking-in of the abdomen will be to your advantage so as to better see the dock or ramp immediately in front of you. For all: It would be well to practice all the steps, beginning with #1, in the privacy of your home. This extra practice will enable you to take your first actual steps on the dock/ramp without the inevitable feeling of self-consciousness that many new boaters feel, causing them to avoid dock-walking in daylight.

2. Look down at the dock/ramp, scanning ahead some 18 to 20 inches for any sticky, smelly, end products of bird, dog, seal or sea lion digestive processes, hereafter called "poop," or ice , snow, or wet spots. Note: In spring, summer or early fall you may skip scanning for ice and snow, except in North Dakota, Minnesota, Buffalo, most New England states, and Canada. After a week of practice, a normal person should be able to scan forward an additional 4 to 6 inches, a necessary skill if you hope to travel at a greater rate of speed. (The word "normal" as used here applies only to the *physical, not mental* persona.)

Tests conducted in major research facilities have shown conclusively that boaters with IQs as low as -8 can attain a more well-developed forward scan in less than two weeks. (To be more specific, 13.528 days. I've rounded the figure up to save space on the paper and avoid excessive use of numbers soon forgotten. The actual figures I've posted for the edification of engineers, CPAs, IRS personnel, and business managers, who tend to question generalities.)

3. From your starting position, move your body forward, while *at the same time* extending the left foot ahead 12 to 14 inches and extending the entire right arm 6 to 8 inches. (All distances have been calculated for a 5'10" person. Those taller or shorter than this must adjust arm and leg distances according to their heights.) WARNING! *If you fail to advance the leg once your weight begins to shift forward, I guarantee you will nullify the good impression you are attempting to create, in addition to having to visit your doctor to treat your newly-broken nose as you fall to the dock!*

4. Allow the left heel to touch the dock or ramp first, followed within a half-second by the remainder of your foot. Do not be concerned about placement, at this time, of your sole and toes, as they generally tend to follow the rest of the foot. However, if yours *don't* follow, my best advice is to visit a podiatrist as soon as possible and avoid any further dock and ramp stepping until after your consultation, treatment, surgery, and recuperation have been successfully completed. Quickly move to step #5 before losing your balance and falling. Sorry to keep you in the awkward #4 position for so long.

   5. Ease your full weight onto the left foot only *after* your foot senses it is securely positioned. Do not stop here. Go directly to #6.

   6. As your body weight finishes transferring to the left foot, begin the dual action of weight forward, right foot advancing while the left arm is swung forward. Repeat steps #4 and #5. Key words: secure, stable feet! This is quite important, especially when a dock is pitching about in large waves, or if strong winds threaten to desta-bilize you.

   7. We've covered the basic step patterns for both right and left feet. Now you need to get somewhere. If you can remember left foot, right foot, left foot, right foot left foot, right foot, in that sequence, YOU WILL SUCCEED! Again, practice in the privacy of your home before your first dock appearance to avoid the herky, jerky appearance of a puppet on a string. That is a sure way of giving to others the appearance of a boating novice.

   A few random, but significant, points for you. Be sure to step UP from a dock to a ramp, but DOWN from a ramp to a dock. A hospital visit will result if you reverse these. Another dangerous time for new boaters is the period of time after they first feel they have mastered the dock/ramp step. A little knowledge is a dangerous thing! New boaters tend to become so exhilarated by mastering the *technique* that they tend to lose their concentration regarding the *destination*, usually the boat. As a result, new boaters have an ex-tremely high rate of accidental immersions, as they step *off the dock* when practicing their correct step technique.

   You might have gained admiring glances for your dock/ramp stepping form, but if others have to pull a soaking wet you back onto the dock, they will realize you are simply a novice, after all. A little trick in case you step off the dock and have to be rescued is to pretend you've just come from a party where you've had too much to drink. *Much* better to have rescuers think you're drunk, not a boating novice!

The final point is, what do you do if you drop something onto the dock? One should never step backwards to retrieve it. Pivot on the balls of both feet simultaneously, and commence the R, L, R, L, R, L etc. pattern of stepping until the dropped object is about 12 inches in front of you. However, if it's in the water, do NOT follow it in! Better to carry a small fish net with you for retrieval.

Figure 1, shown in this chapter, is a visual reminder to help fix my instructions in your mind. Although the dock has been constructed so it's pointing east, and the boat north, it is simply an example. Dock stepping works *in any direction* you may wish to go. You can also step *off* a dock, regardless of its directional heading. It is NOT necessary to carry your compass with you to establish which direction you're walking. I would hate to think you'd step blindly eastward, as shown in Figure 1, when the dock you're on has been built to face another direction, such as south, west, north or something in between, like SSW, NEN or others.

If I haven't made that clear to you, better bring along a change of clothes when you dock/ramp step. You have my permission to cut out the diagram neatly and carry it in your wallet or purse, as a constant reminder that to impress others, you must step well. (Buyers may snip diagram, NOT BROWSERS!)

Figure 1 demonstrates graphically the danger of underestimating the influence of technique over destination awareness experienced by many neophyte dock/ramp steppers. This stepper was obviously inexperienced, as evidenced by the uncertain step pattern. His quotes are fairly standard for this situation.

Figure 1:
   Dock stepper's direction of travel----------------->
"OOPS!"and "Help!" are actual, commonly-used quotes.

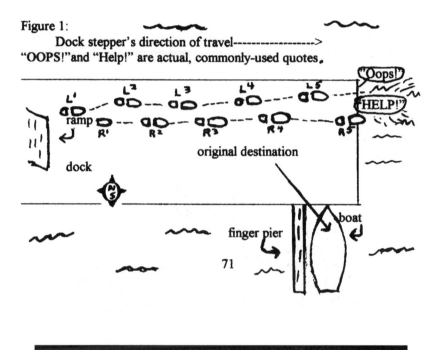

THE TUGBOAT THAT COULD

THE CHRISTMAS DIARY
OF A BOATER'S WIFE

December 26, 1992

Dear Diary: Our first Christmas together! What a beautiful time. Snow everywhere, too much for our parents to come over last night. That's all right, though. Sam outdid himself for me. An Oriental-style robe with silk, embroidered flowers, a matching, *very* skimpy night gown, glad M & D weren't here to see *that!*, and fluffy, warm dragon slippers matched the nightwear. The big surprise was a tiny jewel box containing a 20-carat gold ring surrounding the biggest, most fiery opal I've *ever* seen! It was alive with flashing blues, greens, reds, and golds.

What a man! He really knows what a woman wants. Because he's such an outdoorsman, he loved my gifts to him: a two-burner propane stove for camping trips, a rain suit with waterproof hat and boots, and a set of titanium-faced and graphite-shafted woods to improve his golf game, which frustrated him so much last summer.

December 26, 1993

Dear Diary: Sam's done it again! He hid my old tennis racquet and got me a REALLY large-headed, lightweight replacement. No more tennis elbow, and maybe I can reach some of those shots I've been missing. To go with that, a gorgeous, new tennis outfit, and IT FITS, EXACTLY! I don't know how he knows my sizes so well. The cute, visored cap, with its blue and green piping, is a perfect match for the outfit. I was amazed to open my biggest package and find a warm winter coat. I didn't know he had noticed that my old coat was almost threadbare.

I bought him a two-person Arctic tent for our outings, and as he loves to bring home trout from his fishing outings with his pals, I gave him a huge assortment of artificial flies, hooks, leaders, and lines. So he can get to places on the lake he can't reach now by foot, I got him a tough, inflatable boat with oars and an inflating pump.

73

December 26, 1994

   Dear Diary: Oh, Sam! Where'd you buy the deep-red evening
gown? Red heels, matching jacket, and hat were perfect final
touches. Very classy. My friends will be so envious. We must find
occasions to get out more often. And I *will* take advantage of my
new membership to the health club. Sam hinted last summer that
he'd like a sail kit for the boat I got him last Christmas. Then he
wouldn't have to paddle everywhere and could get to the fishing
holes faster.

   Friends, the Olsens, have a large sailboat and are always
raving about the joy of being under sail, so I got him the whole kit,
mast, tiller, rudder, lines, and *tons* of nuts, bolts, and screws. The
outboard centerboard was quite heavy, but I finally got it wrapped.
Then I got him an electric screw driver, so he's been out in the ga-
rage all day assembling the kit. That's okay, because I've also been
working all day, letting out the seams on the gown and jacket.

December 26, 1995

   Dear Diary: A dreary Christmas. Not much to open from
under the tree, but then, we had agreed the new boat would be our
gift to each other. The inflatable is now our dinghy, and it gets us
safely to shore from our new 29' sailboat, which we named *Victory.*
We've found we both love sailing. The moorage rates are higher
than we thought they' be, but we sail every weekend, and on vacation took a ten-day cruise to the islands. We bought each other float
coats, and four life jackets for friends who might like to sail with us.
Sam and I took the recommended Coast Guard boating course, so
feel much more confident on the water.

December 26, 1996

   Dear Diary: We've been into boating big time this year. Sam
took me and two buddies out to race during the local yacht club's
summer series just to see what it was like. He loves it, but I don't
like to be yelled at when I do something wrong, or too slowly. *He*
can do the racing! Sam bought me a propane stove to replace
Victory's alcohol stove, which scared me every time I tried to light it.
A set of gimbals was perfect, to keep the stove level when we're

heeled over when I'm cooking, which is becoming less frequent while we're underway, as liquids still tend to spill. I cook while we're anchored, mostly. He also got me a sturdy boarding ladder to make it easier to get in and out of the dinghy without falling in, like I did last June. He went in too, when the dinghy tipped up, and we were *frozen* by the time we got back aboard the boat.

I got him a floating flashlight, a radar reflector, a two-way radio, and a satellite-oriented global positioning locator, so we can find out where we are on the charts. Not that we sail out of sight of land. He claims it's important, and keeps tinkering with it. So far, the closest he's located us in comparison to where we *actually* were is about 110 miles away. From where we were sailing I could see the buildings of downtown, so *I* knew where we were, but his little $2,200 gadget showed us in the middle of a U.S. Marine Corps military reservation in the desert on the other side of the mountains. Hah! I hope he's not thinking of sailing to Hawaii or Tahiti!

December 26, 1997

Dear Diary: Whoa! I still remember the Christmases of the past, when Sam was getting me pretty, frilly gifts. Sam and his damn boat!!! He's seriously into racing now, and I stay home while he and his stupid pals race every Wednesday afternoon and several weekends during the year. Now I have a sneaking suspicion that's why he named the boat *Victory.*

Imagine my surprise when I opened "my" gifts last night. Two gallons of bottom paint, (very funny, Sam, when you said it was for the boat, not me. Ha, ha! I was really laughing.), masking tape, a paint pan with two rollers, a sail repair kit with a $20 discount coupon from the local marine supply store, non-polluting soap for swabbing dirty boat decks, collapsible mop with its own bucket, and "my" special gift, a knotmeter.

I had bought him a lapis and gold ring with little anchors carved into it, a special-order captain's cap with gold anchors and braided piping, and a security system for his car. So many cars are being broken into while the guys are way on overnight races. When he saw how disappointed I was, he did take me out to eat. The burgers were good, but the fries were soggy. When I tried to use the new mop on our kitchen floor he told me to stop, as it was for the boat, but he did drive me to the marina the next day to bring the old boat mop home for kitchen use. He said he couldn't tell why I was crying. If he couldn't figure *that* out I wasn't going to tell him!

December 26, 1998

Dear Diary: I was so excited to open our gifts last night! I could hardly wait!! I began to suspect, last year, finally, that Sam was using Christmas "for me" to outfit the boat. Last night proved my every suspicion. As usual, I opened "my" gifts first: a can of teak brightener, a brush for applying it, 12 sheets of wet-dry sandpaper, six tanks of propane, a bosun's chair with all its tackle, 20 feet of one-inch anchor chain, two shackles with their pins, teak floorboards for the cockpit, a kelp cutter, and a large bottle of "Head Cleaner," to keep the boat's head smelling fresh. I professed *much* pleasure. He seemed pleased at my reaction, the total jerk!

I wish everyone could have been here to see the look on his face when he opened my gifts "to him." The first was a one-ounce vial of *Suddenly Spring* perfume, $125 an ounce. He thought it was shaving lotion and thanked me. That was followed by a silky, French uplift bra that "just happened" to be my size, a tooled, Moroccan, camel-leather purse with colorfully inscribed panels, a matching set of emerald earrings, necklace, bracelet, and brooch, four pairs of slips and panties, an assortment of nylons, and a mother-of-pearl mirror and brush set. After gawking in a sort of stunned silence, he finally allowed as how he thought it would be a smart idea to exchange our gifts with each other, if that was all right with me. I appeared to think it over, then reluctantly (Ha, ha!) agreed it wasn't too bad an idea. Then I took him out to dinner.

The Bouef 'de Grazil, Lobster en Nealle, and Potato d'Augustin went well with the Salade Marchande, topped off with one of the last remaining bottles of chilled Saez Monichet, '85, to be found any-where in America. He paid. I truly hope that Sam took the hint for future Christmases, especially after I wore to dinner the lovely evening dress ('94), the coat ('93), the ring ('92), and all the emeralds from this year. A man can't be THAT stupid as to ignore all *those* none-too-subtle hints, or can he? I'll find out next Christmas.

(CLAUDIA'S EFFORT TO BECOME THE FIRST WOMAN TO CROSS THE PACIFIC IN A BATHTUB IS DECLINED BY THE GUINESS BOOK OF WORLD RECORDS)

A BOATER'S IMAGE

One of the major problems boaters face is that of image, as perceived by the non-boating public. As a boater you've heard it all...the drunken boater, the elitist boater, the carousing boater, the polluting boater, the unknowledgeable boater, or the careless boater. You and I, boaters, know that these stereotypical images are, by and large, not true. The average boater is an All-American type, who, steely eyed and iron nerved, faces the challenges of wind, current, water, and storm and conquers them with pride and intelligence while enjoying life to the fullest.

"Hello, viewers. Jim Nolsen here for USBC-TV, profiling today Hank and Delila Sompsan, chosen by the local boating association as the 'Average Boaters of the Year.' As you are well aware, boating has come under severe fire recently from the many non-boating segments of society. Our program today will present both sides of the...Oh! Here's Hank now, supervising the loading of his 45' power cruiser. He and Delila are getting ready for a two-week vacation cruise. Hi, Hank and Delila. Welcome to the show."

"Hi, Jim. Just a second, please. HEY! YOU DELIVERY GUYS! TAKE CARE WITH THOSE CASES! THERE'S LIQUID IN 'EM! Excuse me, Jim. Gotta make sure those guys are careful."

"Right. That's a lot of extra fuel you're loading. But I thought gasoline had to be carried in nonbreakable containers to prevent fumes from igniting in case of breakage. Those containers are glass. Have those regulations been changed lately?"

"Gasoline? That's not fuel, Jim, it's liquor. Wine, brandy, rum, but mostly beer and whiskey. Then, for variety, there's gin, cognac, and vodka...a good assortment. Did I mention the tequila and lots of mixer?"

"No, Hank. That's sure a lot of liquor."

"Well, Jim, we're vacationing on the boat for a full two weeks, and there will be four of us on board."

"Boating's a true family activity, I see. But you're not letting your two children drink, are you?"

"Nah, the kids will be with Grandma and Grampa. We're hosting another couple, long-time acquaintances of ours."

"I see. Fellow boaters, then."

"No, they actually hate boating. Can't stand all the rocking up and down and back and forth when we get out on the water. They get really seasick."

"I don't understand. Two weeks on a cruise? How will they stand *that*? You certainly can't avoid wave action."

"Cruise? Jim, you got it all wrong. We *are* going on a two-week vacation on the boat, but we're not leaving the dock. We'll party right here. Besides, Delila can't walk on the beaches when we dinghy in, with all those sand fleas hopping around and little crabs scuttling underfoot. Isn't that right, Honey?"

"Ooooh! Yucky!" She shuddered, thinking about the sea creatures. "And don't forget about those icky clams squirting cold water up my legs. I get goosebumps just thinking about those creepy, crawly beach things."

"Well, a unique vacation, to be sure. What do you do with all the empty bottles after finishing them off? I know on the dock there's a garbage can, but what about when you're actually on a cruise? Many landlubbers believe boaters just throw them overboard."

"No way, Jim! Nothing, I repeat, NOTHING gets thrown overboard from this boat! There'll be no polluting by anyone on the Sompsan's boat, owner, crew, or guests!"

"Glad to hear that, Hank. How *do* you dispose of the bottles, cans, and garbage that accumulate while cruising?"

"We set them, *very carefully,* on a beach somewhere."

"But isn't that polluting the beach?"

"Wrong again, Jim. The tide comes in twice a day and carries it all off the beach, clean as a whistle. Can't even tell it was there. Our rule is, 'Keep a Clean Beach!'"

"Hmmmm. Hank, what about the image of boaters as elitists, using their boats as status symbols defining their power positions in life? I'd like your opinion."

"Pure bunk! why those, liberal right-wing or left-wing commie-loving dupes who'd say that are simply jealous have-nots. Why, in this country a boat is within reach of anyone who wants one. Remember, there are all types of boats."

"Delila, when you bought this lovely cruiser, how much did it cost, If you don't mind telling our TV audience?"

"It was around $240,000, plus tax, of course. But since then we've added around $30,000 in improvements."

"Isn't that out of the reach of lots of people, most, in fact?"

"Jim, you don't have to spend that kind of money to be a boater. Heck, you can get a good ten-foot rowboat for under $500. After all, a boat's a boat, no matter what its size."

"How'd you two get started in boating? Your Viking blood asserting itself? Or perhaps a sense of historical heritage calling you to our ancestor, the sea? Maybe an adventurous heart that couldn't be satisfied till the challenges of nature were met and mastered? Or a lust for life, urging you into strange and mysterious places, exploring the unknown?"

"No, Jim. What got us started was the neighbor's kid taking those damn loud music lessons and practicing out in their back yard. That great big tuba was bad enough, but when the drum lessons started, the noise drove us out of our house, down to the docks, and finally to our boat purchase. We *had* to get away."

"But Delila, couldn't you complain to the child's parents?'

"No, they were never home. They bought a boat three months before we did. That's them in that blue boat over there by the marina office. They couldn't stand it either."

"Well, Hank, there's certainly a lot of information to know to become a successful and safety-minded boater. Where did you learn the Rules of the Road?"

"Road? Jim, you're sure a landlubber! There's no road out there, no yellow lines or stop signs, just water. True, you do steer like a car, with a wheel, but you don't even have to have a license to operate a boat."

"But I thought the Rules of the Road were set up to govern situations, such as right-of-way, to avoid collisions at sea."

"Ha! Now I see why you're confused, Jim. We never, *ever*, get out to sea. We just boat on lakes, rivers, and the sound, here. Never been on a sea or ocean."

"But Hank, the sea's just a general term for all bodies of..."

"Besides, if it looks like a collision, we just turn up the power and outrun 'em. Speed's the answer on the water. High speed! Gets you out of trouble every time."

"Hank and Delila, I can see now why you were chosen the 'Average Boaters of the Year.'"

"Thanks, Jim But actually, the title was 'Subaverage Boaters of the Year'. They must have confused us with submarines, or something like that. Anyway, the selection committee said that Delila and I had won by a landslide. We thought that was pretty impressive."

"I certainly agree with the committee. We must close our interview for now. One last thought from each of you. If you had one basic rule for boaters, or for future boat buyers, what would it be? Delila, you first."

"I'd say bring along a lot more ice than you think you'll need. Nothing worse than a warm mixed drink or can of beer. To be safe, always buy a boat big enough to have a refrigerator, not an icebox. Then, you won't have to worry about running out of ice.."

"Hank, what's your advice?"

"Jim, a rule that's never failed on our boat. Always have a mop and bucket handy for cleaning up the messes those wimps make who can't hold their liquor when the waves start building and the boat starts rocking."

"Thank you both...I think. I've been interviewing Hank and Delila Sompsan, selected this year, by an overwhelming margin, as the 'Subaverage Boaters of the Year.' Jim Nolsen here for USBC-TV."

Editor's Note: The preceding interview was intended only as an April Fools' Day joke. However, the author, editor, and pub-lisher cannot help it if you read it on a day other than April 1. The only valid reason for having liquor aboard a boat would be to use the corked empties as personal flotation devices in case someone falls overboard or the boat sinks, as any true boater knows.

PRESTIGE

Like most people who live near water, you have undoubtedly walked on the docks of your local marina, even if you don't own a boat. You looked at the boats, perhaps wonderingly, trying to imagine the histories, the mysteries, or the adventures of each. Here's a huge, ocean-going cruiser. How does one earn the millions to buy, crew, and keep up this behemoth? What famous people and celebrities must it have had aboard? Here's a 35-footer with six feet of kelp dangling from its undersides. Why has so little care been taken? Next to it an 18-foot sailboat tugs impatiently at its mooring lines, clearly impatient to be underway. Are the owners racers?

You've seen all sizes and shapes of boats, sail and power. But, have you looked at the people who own these boats? Or talked to them? Or even seen them? Let's do it. Boaters don't mind if absolute strangers approach them to ask questions. They'll talk to anyone, as long as it's about their boats, much the same as exotic-car owners about their cars, or pet owners about their pets...

Here I am at the Seashell Marina and Yacht Club. It's one of those days, blue skies with a few small, cotton-puff clouds floating lazily about, that makes one wonder why every boat in the marina isn't out on the water. Only a few owners are on their boats, scrubbing bird droppings off the decks, brightening up the teak trim, testing equipment and engines, or doing any of the innumerable tasks boaters love to do to keep their boats "shipshape" while moored. I see the harbormaster in the marina office, so I'll go in.

"Good morning, Sir. I'm Si Morner, a writer, doing an article on boat owners. I'd like your permission to walk the docks and interview some, with their permission, of course."
"Avast there, Si. Okay with me, but you'd have better luck staying right here talking to them. Save you a lot of steps."
"You mean they'll be coming in to pay their moorage fees here in the office?"
"Naw, most of them mail those in. They come in mostly to

85

complain about the fees, boat license costs, seagulls and swallows crapping all over their decks, garbage and oil in the water, noisy sea lions and seals, or moldy boat interiors. You name it and someone's complaining about it. Then, about ten or twenty come in every day to see if they've moved up on the moorage waiting list. See this last name on the list? At the present rate it'll be four years before there'll be an opening for him."

"I see hundreds of names on the list. If so many are complaining, why don't they go elsewhere to find moorage?"

"There's a prestige factor, a mystique, an ego builder having to do with mooring a boat here. The Seashell Marina and Yacht Club is a very prestigious one, probably comparable to a golfer mentioning a membership at Pebble Beach or Augusta. Really hard to get in. Some people would kill for moorage here. It impresses a lot of people, kind of like being a rock star or a pro athlete. Then, when they do get in, many ignore their boats. Some haven't taken their boats out for years. You'll see lots of seaweed growing on a lot of hull bottoms."

"I see. The challenge is getting into Seashell for bragging rights. The boat is merely the ticket to get in. I see some people on the dock. Better go. Thanks for your thoughts."

I took my leave and went down the ramp to the dock. A tanned man stood inspecting the bow of a monstrous ocean cruiser. White leather boat shoes, white duck trousers, neatly pressed, a navy blue jacket over a horizontally striped red and white shirt, topped by a billed cap loaded with knotted, gold, braided anchors and dolphins suggested great wealth and power. Here indeed was a captain of industry. I tried to place the face, but couldn't.

"Good morning, Sir. Si Morner here, doing an article on boaters. Do you have a few minutes to talk?"

"G'morning. Two minutes, no more, I'm in somewhat of a hurry just now."

"Thanks. I know your time must be valuable. Can you tell me the length of this beautiful boat?"

"It's 90 feet, stem to stern. Launched in Boston three years ago, and sailed here with a crew of fourteen through the Panama Canal last month. She's worth $13,000,000, has eight staterooms, each with its own head and shower, completely air-conditioned, has two saunas, two hot tubs, and a 24-foot lap pool on the forward deck. Has a wet bar and dance floor in the main salon. Been around the world once and all over Europe and the Mediterranean several times."

"Thanks for all the information. You've anticipated most of my questions about the boat. It's good to hear about someone actually using his boat. How do you find all that time away from work to travel so constantly?"

"Well, when one is wealthy, one delegates people to run the home and branch offices. I forgot to tell you there's a complete business office just aft of the bridge. Computers, faxes...it's all there for him to stay in touch. He's never out of touch, wherever he's cruising, which is most of the time as he checks his worldwide holdings."

"Excuse me. He?"

"Mr. Kenfler, the owner."

"The owner? You mean *you're* not the owner?"

"Oh, no. Even if I won the lottery I couldn't afford this."

"But...your uniform...and your knowledge of the boat.."

"The uniform? I'm the doorman and night bartender at the Seashell Marina and Yacht Club. Believe me, when I take my turn as bartender, Mr. Kenfler gives me an earful about this boat. Every day for 32 days and nights now, an earful. He's so proud of this boat. Thank God he and his boat are departing shortly for Hawaii. I'll be so glad when he sails off."

"But you were about to step aboard."

"I'm here to let Mr. Kenfler know that the brunch at the club-house is ready. Excuse me."

THE LAW OF THE SEA

The sea has called to mankind since the dawn of history. Legendary are the stories of sailors battling howling winds and towering waves, with stove-in hulls battering against lonely, rocky coastlines. Sadly, we recall the oft-occurring horrors of entire crews meeting their watery dooms in failed efforts to escape the wrath of angry seas. We visualize the toppled masts and torn, thundering sails, the rudderless hull beginning its jerking slide beneath the frothing breakers. And there, on the rising stern, the freezing sea clawing relentlessly ever higher towards him, the grim-faced captain awaits eternity. With a prayer on his lips and thoughts of home and family in mind, he stands resolutely, answering the final law of the sea. A last, wrenching wave thunders against the hull, and he, his valiant crew and the ship's crushed carcass join Neptune's dark realm forever.

The sleek, white cabin cruiser *Northwind* ghosted into the small cove. Its well-tuned engine purred softly. Jean Wolden expertly nosed its bow into the dying breeze, while at the bow, husband Glen lowered the anchor, chain, and line to the bottom.

"Okay Jean. Anchor's down. I'll pay out more line." She reversed the engine and backed *Northwind* to set the anchor.
"That's it...a little more...there. You can cut the engine."
"Is it well in, Dear? We're pretty close to shore."
"Should be all right. Plenty of scope out. What a great spot to anchor! No one around, and I hear there's plenty of rockfish and crab here. How does fresh fish sound for dinner? Or cracked crab?"
"Sounds...Glen, look! There's a seal swimming towards us.. No, wait! I believe it's a man!"
"Looks like he's coming in from out in the sound. The tide's against him. Bet he's tired...and cold."

The swimmer raised an arm and waved weakly. A faint "Help!" reached their ears. A wavelet caught and gagged any further words as he slowly dog-paddled towards them. Glen raced to the stern and unhooked the life ring. With a strong toss, he heaved it, the uncoiling

89

line forming spiral patterns till it landed near the tiring swimmer, who hooked an arm into it. Glen hauled slowly, the taut line sending sprays of salt water at each tug.

"Jean, take the line and cleat it down. I'll jump down to the swim platform and help him up. Here's a hand. Come on...up we come...Oof! That water adds a lot of weight. Come on up onto the deck. Step carefully."

"Th...Th...Thanks so much. I needed a favor."

"I guess you did. You're actually blue from the cold swim you took. Around here, people usually don't last more than ten minutes in the water this time of year."

"Glen, I'll get a blanket up here and heat up some coffee. I'll be right back."

"I'm Glen Wolden, Mr...er..."

"Not Mr. I'm Captain Thomas Durnes, Captain Wolden."

"Captain? Of a ship?"

"Yes. I won't be staying long. Just need some help."

"Huh? Well, sure. Anything I can do. But I'm just the boat owner, not a captain."

"Aren't you in charge of this ship? Don't you have the responsibility for its safe operation, proper navigation, and the welfare of the crew?"

"When you put it that way, I suppose I am the captain, but there's no crew, just my wife."

"Just your wife! Do you mean she doesn't assist you in all aspects of the ship's operation? Just your wife! Indeed! she's crew in every sense of the word!"

"You're right, Tom. She's an excellent sailor, and..."

"Please, Captain Wolden. It's Captain Durnes, of the late 31-foot ship *Water Witch*. We hit a log at high speed just beyond the point and opened a hole in her hull. I tried to save her, but water poured in faster than the pump could remove it. She went down, but very gracefully, I might add."

"You said 'we' just now. Are there others involved?"

"No. 'we' is just my ship and me. We were one in spirit. But the favor I need."

"Yes, you mentioned a favor when you first came aboard."

"As with any good, responsible ship's captain, I feel a strong urge to go down with my ship, but I couldn't. I'm wearing one of those new vinyl air jackets under my shirt and I can't get it off. The locks are in the back. I saw you anchor here, so I swam over here to borrow a knife."

Glen's jaw dropped in amazement. "Captain Durnes, do you mean you're going to stab yourself, instead?"

"Of course not. I'll go down in the traditional fashion. I need the knife to slit the air cells in the jacket. Then I'll jump overboard and do the honorable thing by my ship."

"But Tom...er...Captain Durnes, there's no need to die. I've already rescued you. We'll take you back ashore."

"Captain Wolden, you don't seem to understand. All the old-time sailing captains established the tradition. *They* all followed their ships to the bottom. It became almost a *law* among seafarers of all nations of the world."

"That's because it was women and children first into the life-boats. There wasn't room left for the men. Besides, there wasn't usually anyone around to rescue them, like I have you. They were commonly wrecked in places no one could reach them, like Cape Horn, North Atlantic Ocean, or almost *any* stormy place. No radios then, either. Thanks, Jean...I mean...First Mate. Here, Captain, wrap this blanket around yourself. First Mate will have coffee up shortly. I can smell it from here. I'll go below and find a knife and a dry jacket for you. Come over here, out of the breeze."

Glen stepped below and whispered to Jean. "Listen carefully, Hon. We've got a real head-case aboard. His boat went down, and he thinks he's got to go down with it. When I go topside you call the Marine Police Patrol. They're never very far away. Then turn on the masthead strobe light flasher. Tell the police to look for us in Dogfish Bay. Tell them to hurry. I'll try to stall the Captain."

Glen found a warm jacket and the dullest knife he could locate and returned topside. He could hear Jean beginning her call. "Ah, Captain Durnes, let's get this down jacket onto you. You'll get pneumonia, the way you're shivering." He handed the knife to the icy ex-skipper.

"Thanks. I've got the shirt buttons undone. Here, I'll try to slit these air cells in front. Mph! MMMph! UUUH! This vinyl is really thick. Don't believe I made a dent in it at all. OUCH! Knife slipped...Nicked my chin. Do you have any paper towels? I don't want to bloody your deck. That would be too bad after all you've done for me."

"I'll go below and get some. Better hold your head outside the lifelines till I get back." He was back quickly, wadded the towels, applied direct pressure to the wound, and stanched the flow.

"Let's see. I'd better cut from the top downwards, this time. Don't want to put out an eye. Captain Wolden, it would help if you'd be kind enough to hold the top of the jacket. MMMMPH! This is really tough stuff. And I think your knife's dull."

"Let's try this instead. Take your shirt off all of the way, and I'll undo the locks in back. That'll be faster, and you won't go into shock from loss of blood. Besides, this way, you can do some good in this world by donating the undamaged life jacket to some poor, underprivileged boater. I'll donate it in your name."

"Great idea! Here's my shirt off. Can you undo the locks? The instructions are printed right on the vinyl."

"I'm sure on it. Let me read...Let's see... okay. Push Tab A downwards and rotate it towards the left. Nope, didn't work. Wait, here's a tab on the other side. Depress tab B and rotate to the right till arrows are aligned. Okay...nope...maybe Tab A needs some kind of alignment."

"Captain Wolden, I think I've got it. I'll bet you're doing it upside down. The instructions are probably for the wearer. Let me reach around while you guide my fingers to the tabs. Ready? Down and rotate right. Other side...down and rotate left. There! They're free. What a relief! I can go. Thanks so much for your help."

Before Glen could react, Captain Durnes, one hand over his eyes and the other holding his nose, leaped nimbly over the lifelines, arms and legs tightly together in a splash-producing cannonball dive. Glen watched, horror-stricken, as Durnes went under, but was startled as Durnes' head popped up again out of the water, a look of disgust on his face.

"Captain Durnes, what happened? Changed your mind?"

"Can't stay down. These canvas sailors' pants I have on filled with air as I hit the water, and are acting exactly like a life preserver. Can you give me a hand up? There. Thanks."

"Are you going to take your pants off and try again?"

"No. After all, when they find my body I want to have *some* measure of decency. You're a fisherman, I see. Do you have any heavy lead weights aboard? The weight would overcome the resistance of the air in the pants."

"But if you just did a plain, headfirst dive the air wouldn't fill your pants from the bottom. Maybe a little, but not enough to keep you from coming back up."

"No, I was never much good at diving. Always got water up my nose. But considering the circumstances, guess I can give it a try. So long again. Please say goodbye to your First Mate for me."

Jean appeared at that instant with a mug of steaming coffee. She had heard the previous comment and quickly foresaw what was about to occur. She saw Glen tensing to grab Durnes before he could jump. "Captain Durnes, wait!"

"Yes, First Mate?"

"You can't jump if you haven't made plans to dispose of your assets and property. Do you have a will?"

Durnes shook his head no, stepped back onto the deck, and gratefully accepted the coffee. Glen whispered, "Were you able to contact the police?"

"Yes," she whispered back, "they should be here soon." She skipped below and returned with paper and pen in hand.

"All right, Captain. Date the paper, and list the assets have and who gets what. Glen and I will witness for you and make sure the will gets to your next of kin. Also, put down where they may be reached to assist us in contacting them."

"My hands are so cold I can't write. If it's all right with you, I'll just dictate if you'll write. I, Thomas Durnes, being of sound mind and body...that *is* the way I should start, isn't it?" Both nodded yes, even though they disagreed with the truth of the statement in his case. "To continue, then, leave all my earthly property and assets to Hortense."

"Captain, we must have a last name, or every Hortense who hears of this will be after your estate. So, Hortense...who?"

"Hortense is my cat. I suppose Hortense Durnes is enough. I've never thought of a middle name for her. And add this: Whose care I entrust to my mother, Maybelle W. Durnes. That should do it. I'll try to sign it. Fingers're so cold I can barely move them." He struggled, hands purple, to sign.

The three had their attention drawn to *Northwind's* port side as the police cruiser, red lights flashing, powered towards them. It slowed and moved smartly alongside. Two bronzed, uniformed officers stepped aboard, lines in hand, and cleated the two boats together. The taller one spoke.

"Officers Nelson and Bertrand at your service. Got your call of the sinking. Any witnesses or survivors?"

"Glen and Jean Wolden, Officers. We own this boat. And this is Captain Thomas Durnes, skipper of the ship *Water Witch*, now at the bottom of the sound. He was the sole passenger and survivor of the sinking. Now he wants to jump in and go down to be with his boat."

"Captain Wolden, please. It's *ship!*"

"Okay. His ship sank, and we've been trying to stall him till you got here to take him ashore, hopefully for a mental evaluation." Glen whispered the last part of his statement.

"Mr. Wolden, what do you have against a ship's captain going down with his ship?"

"What? There's no reason for it. He wants to join his ship at the bottom because the old-time sea captains did it. They couldn't be rescued. He was. He doesn't have to die."

Officers Nelson and Bertrand both paused, as if in deep thought. Officer Nelson drew a citation book from his coat pocket. Bertrand spoke. "Mr. Wolden, you admit rescuing Captain Durnes, then? I need to remind you that you have the right to remain silent."

"*I* have the right to remain silent? If you're talking to me, yes, I threw him a life ring, pulled him out of the water, and here he is now, wanting to jump right back in!"

The officers glanced at each other. Nelson addressed Glen. "Mr. Wolden, I'm sorry to tell you this. You meant well, but you're under arrest. You've broken the law. Anything you say may be used against you in a court of law. You are allowed one phone call, to be monitored by either of us. I imagine it will be to your attorney. These calls usually are.."

Glen and Jean reacted as may have been expected at this turn of events. Glen caught his wits first. "Officer, You're joking! What have I done to get arrested?"

"The charge will be preventing a ship's captain from going down with his ship."

"Officer, that's no law. It was just an old-time tradition."

"Mr. Wolden, it's law now. Both the city and county councils passed laws last Spring that legalized boat owners going down with their boats...er...ships. Seems just anyone can go buy and operate a boat, without a license even, but not many know how to operate them safely or even care for them so they'll stay seaworthy. The councils' treasuries were going broke sending the marine patrols out on huge numbers of rescue missions, so they passed what's called the 'Distressed Boaters Law.' Overtime was draining their budgets, fast! In fact, by May, the city and county were almost out of money, and summer hadn't even started yet. And that's our heaviest season for boat rescues. We've been on the go all the time since then.."

Jean glared at the two , then spoke heatedly. "That's the stupidest thing I've EVER heard! I can't *believe* what I'm hearing! This is an outrage!"

"Easy, Mrs. Wolden. That's bordering on verbal assault of a police officer. And oh yes, did you or did you not prepare the cup of coffee Captain Durnes is holding in his hands?"

"Why, yes I did! And I loaned him that down jacket and gave him that blanket because he was so blue with cold and shaking so hard he could barely stand up!"

"Jean, STOP! Don't say another word till we call our attorney! I don't want *you* involved in this."

"Ma'am, I believe you're owner, too, but if you abetted this crime, that is, made the coffee at the command Of Captain Wolden here, you'll probably be able to plead *pro extremis venis* at your trial and get off with only six months of community service. But if you supplied the coffee, blanket, and down jacket on your own, you could get the same as your husband, three to five years, with time off for good behavior of course." Officer Nelson shifted his feet uncomfortably as he said this, and neither officer could look the Woldens in the eyes. It seemed they were not in agreement with this law.

Jean spoke again, sugar-sweetly this time. "Can you explain to me once more why I'm suddenly a criminal for giving a cup of hot coffee and helping this poor man overcome hypothermia? My brain's not accepting this outrage very easily."

Officer Nelson rolled his eyes and recited again. "Both local governing councils have honored the long-established tradition of a sea captain's right to go down with his ship. They were forced to make this law to keep from going broke. People who don't own boats shouldn't have to pick up the tab for tax money spent on rescuing boaters in trouble. They get very upset, in fact. Therefore, anyone who interferes with that law is obviously breaking it. It's a misdemeanor, bordering on felony. A death or near-death is involved. We didn't make the law, but must enforce it."

"I think the public will be outraged over this, once the publicity gets out. And I'll make sure it gets out!"

"Ma'am, at the hearings only a few people attended. They were mostly middle-aged types, and loved the idea. You know, power of a ship's captain, romance of the sea, historical tradition, all that."

Glen had been deep in thought. "Officer Nelson, you suggested the power of a ship's captain. I am owner and now captain of this boat, now a ship. If I order Captain Durnes to jump overboard, and he succeeds in his wish, would those charges against Jean and me be dropped?"

"Yes, Sir, that's right. There would remain a $250 fine for you to pay for our response to your emergency call to us that wasn't a true emergency."

"But I honestly believed that saving a man's life *was* an emergency. What *does* constitute an emergency?"

"Well, there's shipboard fire, of course, and crew mutiny."

"And I suppose, without having studied this law, that one should stand idly by while watching it burn without helping those aboard or who'd jumped into the water. And what about those that truly wished to be rescued?"

"Remember, Mr. Wolden, that the law applies only to the *captain* of the vessel in trouble. Passengers, if they wish to be rescued, have to sign a special disclaimer form, which releases the rescuer from all liability at any time during the rescue. It's on a specially - prepared sheet of waterproof paper that you can pick up at any marina office, city hall, or attorney's office. You obviously don't have one with you, so we'll have to add $50 to your fine for failing to have a 'Rescuer's Liability Release Form' aboard. That was part of last year's boating law changes. But the captains who want to go down with their ships and are determined, don't have to sign anything. They're allowed to just...sink...on their own. A nice last gesture, don't you agree?

"Great," murmured Glen. "But I haven't noticed many boat fires around this year. This whole thing looks like a poor piece of legislation and a waste of the councils' time."

"Oh, no Sir," from Officer Bertrand. "Why just this morning we prevented a shipboard mutiny!"

"On a pleasure boat? I've never heard of that before."

"This was on a 65-footer. The owner had about a dozen guests aboard, and the freezer generator had gone out."

"Starvation, eh? Yes, I can see *that* as an emergency."

"Oh, they had other food, chips, dips and loaves of bread and so forth. No danger of starving. But all the ice cubes for their mixed drinks had melted. They became angry at the owner and threw him overboard. Luckily we got there in time, and had him sign the release form even though the boat wasn't sinking. We pulled him aboard and escorted the ship, guests and all, back to the owner's moorage. Mutiny's pretty serious, Sir."

"I've had enough! As captain of this ship I hereby order Captain Durnes into the water, carrying these two six-pound weights. I'll take back the down jacket, Captain. You won't need it where you're going! Goodbye, Sir. Officers, please assist him overboard and have your Liability Release Forms ready for him to sign if and when he pops up again. That should drop the charges against Jean and me."

Captain Durnes looked gratefully at Glen. Thanks, Captain Wolden and First Mate. I'll never forget you for what you've done for me today. Officers, drop all charges against these two. I'm ready. Goodbye."

He stepped to the swim platform and poised to jump, lead weights in hand. A wave broke over his purple feet. He paused, turned, and faced them. "I've changed my mind. It *is* mid-October. The water's too cold, and I'm freezing. I've decided to do this next summer, after the air and water have warmed up a bit.

THE GEODUCK: FACT OR MYTH?
An Essay - of Sorts

The State of Washington, tucked away as it is in a corner of the U.S.A., is as yet relatively undeveloped. It takes a driver only minutes, once the metropolitan areas have been left behind, to be in the midst of forested hills, rugged mountains, or long stretches of lonely beaches. Because of these vast open areas of unpopulated desolation, Washington plays host to several superstitions: The Sasquatch, a furry being no one has ever seen; the steelhead, a fish that no one has ever caught; and the geoduck, either a bird or a gigantic mollusk, said to resemble a clam on steroids, that no one has ever dug or eaten. The first two mentioned have been discussed in depth innumerable times in magazines, newspapers, and at scientific seminars, with wide divergence of opinions as to their being actual living things of nature.

Without corroborating evidence of any kind, such as hair caught by a bush, or observation by trained, competent, reliable, and sober witnesses, Sasquatch was not mentioned one time at last month's meeting of the New World Society of Natural Science seminar, held in Seattle. The subject of the steelhead did arise, but with only one scientist, Dr. Ray Piscatore, speaking for the possibility of this rumored species, the debate was quickly ended. By a 216-1 vote, the one vote being Dr. Piscatore's, the assembled body reaffirmed its no-steelhead position.

In his impassioned, pro-steelhead argument, Dr. Piscatore claimed to have actually caught, landed, and eaten (at home, cooked) a seven-pounder just this past winter, an idea pooh-poohed by the entire membership, many of whom having spent long hours in knee-deep, wintry, icy, body-numbing rivers, in their unsuccessful attempts to land one to prove its existence. Most, if not all, had quit this futile exercise, finally realizing that they had been duped by fishing tackle salesmen in their efforts to buoy up store sales during the cold winter months, when any *sane* fisherman is comfortably resting at home on a sofa watching TV.

When goaded by the other scientists to produce evidence of the fish in question, Dr. Piscatore claimed the pictures taken by his wife of himself holding the huge trout showed only *his* head from the neck up, due either to poor camera-aiming skill on his wife's part or the fact that she was shivering so hard the camera was bouncing up and down, and missed the fish, the most important part of the picture. He went on to claim the family had eaten the delicious flesh for dinner, but that Mrs. Piscatore had inadvertently thrown the head, bones, tail, fins, and guts into the garbage. His testimony, so resembling the sightings and pictures of the Loch Ness Monster and Sasquatch, later proved to have been faked, drew a veritable symphony of catcalls, boos, and hisses, with calls of "fraud," "imposter," and "humbug" clearly heard in the hall.

Dr. Piscatore, stung by his colleagues' criticism, rose, and in an angry speech vowed never to return to another of the group's meetings until he had caught another steelhead for their personal viewing and positive identification. He then stomped out, another chorus of mocking calls ringing in his ears. He is not expected by any to return. Ever.

Having dismissed those two myths, that leaves the little-known geoduck as a yet-unstudied subject for verification by science. You may ask, why is the geoduck included as a yet-unstudied subject in a book designated for boaters, landlubbers, and regular, normal people? Please read on.

Porcupines have been accorded federal "safe conduct", that is, protected status, as they go about their business, whatever that may be, but with one exception. Because porcupines are so slow-footed, a lost, starving hiker may kill one for eating, thereby surviving. There are, of course, *real* problems for the poor hiker to overcome and be able to live by eating one:
    1. To find a porcupine
    2. To capture one, particularly one that doesn't wish to be captured, a common survival trait among porcupines
    3. To avoid the forceful swipes of its quill-laden, barbed tail
    4. To get past the quills to the skin

5. To get past the skin without an extremely sharp knife
6. To get a fire going without matches in an area of the world known for its constantly wet wood
7. To repulse the fierce, vengeful attacks of the victim's kinfolk and friends.

As a matter of fact, most lost hikers never even get to step #1, and few are willing to take on the daunting task of fighting an angry porcupine, which is step #2. As an unfortunate consequence, there are undoubtedly far more dead, formerly lost and starving hikers than dead porcupines. As of yet, however, no federal laws as strong as those protecting porcupines have been passed by congressional lawmakers in support of lost and starving hikers.

The recently concluded discussion shows just what a porcupine *could* be to a lost, starving hiker. Likewise, a geoduck, *if* it does exist, could serve as a meal to a lost, starving boater, cast upon a beach by a severe storm. In addition to worrying about his or her boat, the castaway boater has a dilemma in that he or she must make a decision either to fashion a net out of vines to snag the geoduck, if it is a bird, or dig down into the sandy beach for one, if it a mollusk, as the weight of local lore suggests. And what about the word "lost", as in lost boater? Lost? on a wide open beach? If you've never been on a Washington State salt water beach *any* time of the year, you cannot remotely imagine the ground-hugging, dense, smothering fog that envelops square miles at a time, totally eliminating all sense of direction. This fog, most days of the year, days and weeks at a time, hangs relentlessly, like a clammy, cold blanket, heavy with moisture.

As an example of its density, let us examine the true story of Dr. A.T. Fresburg, mollusk specialist, on a recent geoduck-hunting expedition to Washington's Olympic Peninsula coastal beaches. As the large expedition hiked the beach, Dr. Fresburg became separated from the main body of the party in the lowering fog. His calls for help went unnoticed, his voice vibrations being reflected back to his own ears by the almost solid wall of water vapor particles.

Dr. Fresburg, nicknamed "Fidel" because of his scraggly beard and penchant for long Cuban cigars, finally spotted a light through

I'M <u>NOT</u> LOST...I JUST CAN'T SEE THROUGH THE FOG...

the fog. He hiked happily towards it, hoping to find a house and telephone. After a half-hour's walk, however, he was startled to find that the light he thought of as his salvation was actually the lighted end of his cigar, which had become visible only as it burned within three inches of his nose. The temperature dropping rapidly below freezing, the entire fog bank began solidifying. Using the folding geoduck shovel he carried on his belt, he hacked his way upwards through the congealing fog, some 100 feet, in order to be able to breathe at the top of the bank. After spending a miserable night on what was now solid ice, he descended the next morning as the air temperature rose, thawing the frozen fog and returning it to its usual misty state.

The members of the expedition were able to locate him only when they smelled his cigar smoke as he passed within a few feet. At that, it was only by a simple majority vote, as the nonsmokers voted as a bloc, to allow him to continue onward to rid themselves of the fetid odor.

As the scientists sat around the evening camp fire for the final time, after two weeks of unsuccessful attempts to locate the mythical geoduck, they brainstormed ideas to present later as the theory we think of now as "The Geoduck: Another Steelhead? Another Sasquatch? Another Loch Ness Monster? Theory." Their major premises, leading to their final, unassailable conclusion, will be presented at the Society's next meeting.

Some of the premises were leaked to the author by a disgruntled scientist, who was forced by luck-of-the-draw to be tentmate with Dr. Fresburg and his cigars for the full two weeks. You are privy, here and now, to a preview of what will be presented at that meeting. We were fortunate to have a camera handy for a group picture, before their departure back to their respective university research labs and centers. The tall, distinguished looking man is Dr. Forey Sands, expedition leader.

Dr. Fresburg is on the left, almost out of the picture, as he was down to the last half inch of his two-day-old cigar, and it was pretty powerful smoke! As it was a foggy day, even though it had partially lifted, you must look carefully to make them out. We here at Happy Hills hope you get as much satisfaction as we did in viewing them, as there are so few opportunities to view such a significant body of mollusk researchers on an expedition.

Their premises and conclusions:

1. Life forms, from the very simple to the very complex, strive to live to their fullest potential.

2. Even the simplest forms, for example, amoebas, will try to adjust to their environments in the safest ways of living that accord the optimum chance of survival, including basic, instinctive, and defensive reactions against perceived enemies.

3. We must agree that all forms of life have intelligence of high degrees inherent in the complexities of the species.

4. Washington's saltwater beaches, fogged in heavily most of the year and consisting mainly of sand, gravel, mud, and rocks, would preclude any form of *intelligent* life forms from existing there. Even birds are found to avoid these fog-bound sites, possibly why the *duck* part of geoduck carries more weight as to the true nature of the animal, *if* it exists at all.

5. The geoduck, rumored to live deep in the mud of these beaches, must have enough intelligence to dig deep, its survival defense, to avoid the hostile environment, EXCEPT,

6. That the beach mud, with the consistency of nearly-dry cement, precludes digging. Even if the geoduck could dig that deep, it would go against all law of nature for it to dig itself three or four feet down, only to entomb itself forever in a gloomy, self-made prison with no chance of escape.

7. No one in the expedition has, in two weeks of intensive

digging, been able to locate a geoduck. Likewise, the expedition's small-mesh nets have been unable to snare a bird of any species.

8. While clam shells of smaller species were found on the beaches in abundance, NOT ONE gigantic mollusk shell has been recovered for study.

9. All species of mollusks identified by science are recognized, through their siphons, to produce squirts of water, some reaching as high as one foot into the air. Not one *large* squirt, which may be reasonable from such a reputedly large mollusk, has been observed and documented by anyone in the expedition. This in itself goes against usual mollusk behavior, and is damning evidence against the possibility of the geoduck's existence.

10. Because of the weight of the evidence, even the *lack* of certain behaviors usually associated with mollusks, we, as a body, reluctantly but safely conclude that the geoduck exists only in the gullible, shallow minds of those who believe in the Tooth Fairy, the Easter Bunny, Santa Claus, Sasquatch, Steelhead, the Yeti, and the Loch Ness Monster.

The members of the expedition broke camp in the fog, stumbled from the beach bivouac along the forest path back to their vans, and returned to civilization. Without the men and women of the expedition stomping about, shouting to one another, and digging holes here and there on the beaches, a strange sight began to occur on the tideflats. From hundreds of openings pushing up from deep in the muddy sand, solid sprays of water blew three and four feet into the air, almost as in celebration of the party's departure. At least that's what *I'd* like to believe. But even had you been sitting on the beach you'd not have seen this magnificent display, assuming there *is* such a thing as a geoduck, being denied by the pea-soup mantle of fog.

The geoduck, unless a future expedition proves otherwise, will remain haunting our minds as to its existence. Unofficially it exists, but only as a pre-historic Indian legend, fostered, undoubtedly, by those who would stimulate tourism in this great state.

THE LOST BOATER/BEACH HIKER
Eating for Survival

The previous chapter hinted at problems of survival faced by the lost. It would be untoward of me to leave the reader, who may well face that situation at some time in the future, without suggesting means of ensuring survival at sea or on the beach. The implications of the previous chapter's scientists' recommendations are so clearly evident that I will summarize only briefly, without going into detail. They form, as you'll conclude, a realistic, useful manual for survival when lost.

1. No lost, starving boater/beach hiker should rely on the proven nonexistent geoduck for food. As Dr. Sands, expedition leader, so sagely observed at the final campfire meeting on the fog-ridden beach, "How can you eat what ain't there?" This deep philosophical insight had been greeted with solemn approval by the group, despite their wincing at the realization that not all great mollusk scientists are great grammarians. (In fact, Dr. Sands had spent two years in remedial high school English classes, to no avail, this to be kept secret. Forget you even read it here, to prevent sullying the name of perhaps the greatest mollusk scientist the world has ever known.)

2. Few lost boaters/beach hikers find themselves with an arsenal of survival tools when becoming and after finding themselves lost, for example, axes, shovels, picks, chain saws with gas can and extra spark plugs, dynamite, .30 caliber or larger weapon, and a 40' to 60' length of rope. You will find that a well-sharpened pocket knife may be your method of salvation, along with a first aid kit containing tape, gauze, suture needle and thread, antiseptics, antibiotics, and an extra pint of blood, for the inevitable amputated finger, sliced thigh, or any other body part which can suffer when the knife is used. The knife may be used to sharpen the ends of suitable wood pieces into crude but effective spear points.

3. While using the knife and accidentally (how else, unless you decide hara kiri is the only thing left for you?) spill blood onto the ground, keep a sharp lookout for edible animals, not geoducks, however,

but including porcupines, that may be attracted by the scent of blood to the accident site. Spear throwing takes practice. You must be accurate in delivering the spear to a fatal spot *on the first throw,* or face probable loss of your prey. If you are anticipating a trip by boat or a hike on the beach, you should practice throwing the spear daily in the back yard to develop the necessary accuracy, perhaps at the neighbor's constantly barking dog that's always digging up your bulbs and flowers.

Alternative foods for the lost and starving are many, excluding the nonexistent geoduck, the elusive porcupine, and the mythological steelhead. Here is a listing of your BEST possibilities, often overlooked, as sources of food, while lost on the beach after your boat has been disabled by storm at sea and driven ashore, assuming you have survived:

1. Sandworms -May be eaten raw as found. Can be dug by hand, a plus factor for those who find themselves without a shovel. For the boater whose boat has luckily drifted ashore, with supplies aboard to supplement a sandworm repast, this recipe is included: 10 - 15 sandworms, 10" -14" in length, one sliced tomato, one potato, 1/2 cup milk, one diced onion, and a dash of pepper and salt. May substitute sea water if milk is not available, but hold the salt. A sprig or two of parsley may be added for seasoning. With all ingredients in the pot, bring to a slow boil.

NOTE: For those eating them raw, cut into bite-sized pieces BEFORE eating them. Eaten whole, or wolfed down, in the case of a ravenous starver, they have a marked tendency to resist the stomach's digestive processes. You would get what sandworm eaters call "wiggly stomach" for up to an hour after ingesting, as they make their best efforts to escape.

2. Beach Fleas - Found abundantly on Washington's beaches, they are nearly 100% protein. Eaten like popcorn, they are crispy and crunchy. After placing one or more in your mouth, close it quickly, as they tend to hop towards the light of an open mouth. Once it is closed, however, they tend to fall asleep quickly, thinking it to be night time, and are easily chewed and swallowed.

3. Whales - Whales are not known for their willingness to beach themselves simply to provide a starving boater or beach hiker with a VERY large meal. This source of food, then, creates a unique situation for the starving. Knowing that whales are protected by international treaties, it takes a callous, scofflaw of a starving boater to capture and use one, that is, part of one, for a meal.

However, starving boaters have been known to do strange things, depending on the length of time since their last meal. Like the porcupine, the whale presents its own sets of problems relating to capture and of cutting into edible portions, carried to the *nth* degree. Great ingenuity is required, particularly by a lone boater, to successfully bring a whale dinner to its conclusion. Any boater quick witted enough to capture one will be rewarded by a lifetime supply of meat and blubber, but only if freezer space can be found quickly enough for the usual 30-40 tons of the behemoth. If the rescue of the boater *is* effected, the whale must NOT be cut free and thereby wasted. By towing the carcass to a town located near the water— Seattle, Edmonds, Bremerton, and Tacoma come to mind—a whale festival and "eat-in," honoring the spirit of the deceased, can bring an entire town, community, county, or state solidly together.

One must allow for at least three days of breakfasts, lunches, dinners, and midnight snacks at this festival, with departing guests receiving 100 to 200 pounds of blubber as going-away gifts. To supplement the meal, organizers should have on hand up to 70 tons of potatoes, 5,000 lemons to squeeze onto the meat to disguise the taste of what eaters thought would be delicious, but was REALLY STRANGE! 500 pounds of salt, 200 pounds of pepper, and 1,000 bottles of ketchup should also be on hand. For those unable to eat whale, a nice gesture, sure to engender good intercommunity feeling, would be to supply the festival with 1,000 pounds of lutefisk along with 300 pounds of melted butter for dipping the lutefisk into. The younger generation can be introduced to this Scandinavian delight by providing lutefisk-on-a-stick, similar in appearance to a Popsicle, but without the tooth-ravaging sugar content.

Those actually *eating* whale must be on constant alert for the Feds. There is a very large fine, in the tens of thousands, depending on how much whale you've eaten, as well as a mandatory 5- to 10-year jail sentence. Promoters of a whale festival and eat-in should be aware of the social upheaval that will occur should an *entire* town, say Olympia, our state capital, be fined and imprisoned, even for only the shorter, five-year sentence.

4. Kelp - Highly nutritious, containing high percentages of healthful minerals. For the squeamish, a morsel of kelp helps swallow a mouthful of beach fleas or sandworm. Kelp, in addition to stalling death by starvation, promotes bright, shiny hair, a peaches-and-cream complexion, increased production of both large and small intestinal secretions, and, for lost teenagers, prevents acne and increases I.Q.s, thus leading to more productive schoolwork, should they be lucky enough to return to civilization. It has been reported, but not yet scientifically substantiated, that kelp also acts as a no-cost re-placement for costly sexual-enhancement drugs, with the added benefit of not requiring a prescription from a doctor.

5. Cambium - layers of trees, also known as the inner bark, especially of cedar trees. Bears *thrive* on inner bark, clawing and ripping the outer bark open to get at this delicious, chewy delicacy. As an added bonus, the bald-headed lost should rejoice in the hope that by eating cambium, a black, bushy, bear-like head of hair might appear, along with virile, black chest hair and eyebrows to die for.

A lost, starving woman, though, is advised to weigh the con-sequences of eating the inner bark, to avoid these follically-advantaged results so important to testosterone-laden men. For women, the amount of bark eaten, if one becomes desperate enough to eat it, should reflect only the amount necessary to sustain life, searching, meanwhile, for other foods less likely to promote shaggy, bristly hair growth in unwanted areas of the body. Blondes should avoid the inner bark entirely to avoid becoming brunettes, or face the consequence of having to buy hair coloring every two weeks to revert to their original blond status.

Both men and women, boaters and beach hikers alike, will find the inner bark best-reached by always having a chainsaw, extra gasoline, and spark plugs along while lost, as the outer bark does present difficulties of penetration. A better option is to locate and utilize a tree previously ravaged by a hungry bear, with its inner bark already exposed.

6. Insects - Ants, spiders, grasshoppers, beetles, wasps, bees, hornets, centipedes, millipedes and termites are found nearly everywhere. Eat these as you would beach fleas, that is, as popcorn, Remember to remove the stingers and poison sacs from the stinging insects BEFORE eating, a very important step for those allergic to stings from these nasty things. Most of the previously-lost-but-now-found boaters, while recounting their insect meals, relate and recommend that the centipedes and millipedes have their legs removed first, *before* eating. The legs tend to keep wriggling long after the creature they were attached to has gone to whatever hereafter awaits its poor soul, and legs create *really* weird sensations down in the small intestines and beyond. Even the most desperate will avoid spiders, preferring to eat dirt first.

7. I have eliminated such dangerous animals as bear, moose, elk, and cougars from consideration entirely. If you have ever faced an irate, charging bull moose, you will know that nabbing a porcupine is comparatively simple, even given *its* related problems. If any of the aforementioned animals are seen by you before they see *you*, the best tactic is to climb the nearest tree and wait till they depart, and satisfy your hunger pangs by downing leaves or the smaller branches, chewing them thoroughly before swallowing. You will discover soon, to your delight, that you will never be constipated again, thereby saving big dollar amounts by not having to purchase laxatives at the drugstore.

8. Skunks, Civet Cats - Under NO circumstances, except facing IMMEDIATE death from starvation, should you attempt a meal of either of these. If you *do* manage to somehow get one into your stomach, you must face the solid fact that if found and returned to civilization, the social isolation you would suffer from the odors you emit, after having tangled with one, would hardly be worth the effort it took for you to capture and eat it to begin with. Try to avoid standing

upwind from *anyone,* even close, loving relatives, including your mother. You're probably better off becoming a hermit! Think *twice* about these two!

The astute reader will undoubtedly think of other four-legged, two-legged, or no-legged meals to be found in nature. *This is a good thing!* That reader is looking ahead, and will be better prepared to survive should the time come that he or she finds himself or herself a lost starving boater or beach hiker. You probably have thought of many other meals not mentioned here, for example, starfish, known to be crunchy, or jellyfish, delicious when broiled and served with lime juice, just to name two other common food sources. Good luck to you, when lost, or should I say "FOOD luck?" Both.

Rough Waters

A FREE OYSTER DINNER

One of the enticing things about boating is that the seas, lakes, rivers, and beaches offer sources of healthful, free food. Time spent fishing, netting, or digging may result in a variety of fish, crabs, clams, oysters, mussels, crayfish, or even seaweed. As civilization encroaches and closes in on threatened species and limited marine populations, great skill must be developed to extract these nutritious, tasty menus from Nature's pantry.

There's nothing better than receiving a dinner invitation from friends, especially when you know it will be a sumptuous feast prepared by a fine cook. Angela and Fred Monclair stood knocking at Dan and Jeannie Kiran's door, anticipating just such a meal. Many times they had traded meals, and as the door opened, a well-known scent wafted to their nostrils, making their mouths water.

"Angela, Fred, hi. Come in. Here, I'll take your coats. Have we got something for you tonight! Jeannie's out in the kitchen, almost ready to serve, so we'll just sit right down."

"Mmm. Oysters! My favorite!" Angela smiled in appreciation for what was about to appear on the table.

"Mine too, Dan. We've hardly seen you two since you bought your boat. Angela's phoned so many times without getting an answer. You and Jeannie've been getting a lot of use out of it, I guess."

"Yeah, we've been having so much fun cruising around. We just got back yesterday, with a bucket of oysters for tonight. Sure glad you could come and help us eat them."

"Dan, what's happened to your hand? Looks pretty serious, all bandaged up like that."

"Pretty bad, all right. When we got home I tried opening those oysters. Used a kitchen knife. Should've used an oyster knife. The doctor had to take 25 stitches in my palm and fingers. They are *super tough* to open. Lucky I have a good health plan. Only had to pay the first $250 deductible. Without that insurance I'd have had to pay nearly $400 because I had to have it done in the emergency room. My doctor was out playing golf and couldn't be reached. If you ever shuck oysters make sure you have an oyster knife, use a

115

leather-palmed glove, and make sure your insurance is current. Might want to make sure oyster shucking is covered by your plan. Mine was, but I guess some don't cover it, kinda like parachute jumping, a dangerous activity."

"Ta da! Here they are. Oysters Rockefeller! Eat all you want. If we were at a fancy restaurant they'd serve only four or five each, and probably cost $90 plus tip. But from Jeannie's kitchen, all you want, free."

"Jeannie, I'm going to have to use the pillow after all. Could you get it and put it on the chair for me? Thanks. That's *so* much more comfortable."

"What's this, Dan? A pillow on the chair? Hemorrhoids?"

"Tell them about the man on the beach, Dan."

"Oh, that crazy hothead. We'd anchored about 75 yards out from the beach, and I rowed the dinghy ashore. I was prying oysters off the rocks when this guy comes running full speed towards me with a shotgun in hand. Claimed I was the fourth boater this week who was stealing his private oysters from his private rock bulkhead, and I had no right to them. Well, I told him where to go and started back towards the dinghy, oysters and shovel in hand. He cuts loose with a load of birdshot. What a crummy shot, lucky for me. Only got ten or twelve BBs in my rear. And what an agonizing row back to the boat! They seemed to dig in with each oar pull."

"You poor guy. But I guess he had the law on his side."

"Guess so. We stopped at the first small town we came to and had a doctor remove the BBs. I'd already met the surgical deductible, but the pharmacist's cost was $110 for pain killer and antibiotics."

"Dear, tell them about the policeman."

"The doctor had to call and notify the local police. Any gun wound has to be reported, but after the facts were out in the open I got off with just a trespassing charge. Those rural cops are hard on 'rich' boaters, but during the hearing I used a few legal tricks I picked up from watching TV and got the judge to cut the fine down to $250 and a suspended sentence. Initially, he was going to fine me $600, with court costs."

"Dan, you mentioned you got the facts out into the open. What kind of facts supported you? Seems to me it was pretty cut-'n-dried that you were guilty."

"The facts were that I was completely ignorant of the beach rights law, and that the homeowner shouldn't have fired the shotgun at me. He got spanked for that, I'll tell you."

"That's a pretty wild story, Dan. I'll bet you learned a lot from it, and it won't happen again."

"Well, that's not all. Dan, tell them about the Fish and Game Department man."

"Right. Instead of just letting us leave after paying the fine, the police called the game warden. I don't know what this country's coming to! They've got laws that don't keep respectable citizens like us from getting mugged, assaulted, and killed on the streets, but remove one oyster from where you got it and ZAP! They've gotcha! Something about baby oysters needing an old oyster shell to attach onto or die. I've heard of being arrested for possession of heroin or marijuana, but whoever heard of getting nailed for possession of an oyster shell? That seems mighty un-American to me, right?"

"I take it you weren't aware of the oyster shell law. Think I read about it somewhere."

"*Completely* naive, Angela. So anyway, there's this REALLY BIG fine, but when I told the warden I wasn't aware of the law and promised to never let it happen again, he cut the fine down to $100. But then he nicked me $75 for having too many oysters over the limit."

"Mighty generous of him. Seems like a reasonable guy."

"Yes, except he told us he'd appreciate it if we never showed our faces in those waters again. Told us to read up on the fishing and shellfish regulations and learn them. Said we were giving boaters a bad reputation. But that's all past now. Let's enjoy the meal. Nothing like having free oysters from the sea, and fresh, too."

"Yes, true. But Dan, old buddy, you've told us that you paid nearly a thousand dollars in fees, fines and medical costs to get these oysters here onto our plates. I count 32 oysters on the serving tray. That's roughly $30 per oyster. Then there's boat operating costs, gas and oil, and moorage fees. Doesn't seem to me that these tasty morsels are free."

"Fred, just stop and think for a moment. Let's say we're eating at a nice restaurant downtown. We have gas and oil for the car to pay, plus $20 for parking. Tips for the parking valet, headwaiter, and waiter. Dinner, plus a couple of rounds of drinks'll bring it up to maybe

$300. Then, whenever we go out, Jeannie has to have a new dress, matching shoes, and purse. There's another $300. And it must be worth a couple of hundred dollars just to get out of the house with friends and spend a relaxing evening away from the TV, telephone solicitors, and general neighborhood noise."

"But Dan, that's not..."

"Fred, just shaddup and eat your dinner."

Dinner over, the foursome sat in the living room, catching up on each other's lives and gossiping the way old friends do. Angela put both hands on her abdomen and moaned.

"Jeannie, I don't feel well at all. I'm getting sick to my stomach, and my lips tingle. My tongue feels funny too, almost like it's paralyzed."

"Angela, me too. Anyone else feeling bad?"

Both men nodded yes. "Dan, did you check for red tide before you picked the oysters off the rocks?"

"Red tide? What's that?"

"Some kind of poison or toxin or something that gets into shellfish. Doesn't harm them, but eating them can be deadly, even fatal, for humans. I just read about it in the newspaper. Angela's symptoms are typical of it. We'd better get to the emergency room at the hospital. Probably have to have our stomachs pumped. Let's go, NOW!"

"My fault. I'll drive us there, c'mon. Fred, is your medical insurance current?"

"Yes, but I'll have to pay the $250 deductible, Bah!"

"Fred...Angela...Know what? I've been thinking. Maybe better the restaurant for $90."

A CONVERSATION AT THE MARK

Sailboat racing is a sport in which gentlemen and ladies compete in finely tuned boats, a sport in which only the highest ethical character is in evidence. It has been only in recent years that women's racing has enjoyed its explosive growth, with all-women crews competing successfully in local, national, and international regattas, showing the same noble traits as the men. Spectators, being on the shore and away from the action, miss the stimulating, spirited repartee between the racers during the exciting moments in the heat of the action.

Let's re-create the color of the action at a mark, that is, for the uninitiated, a buoy or other visible, anchored object marking one portion, or leg, of the racecourse, usually used as a turning point. These are critical sites, where instant decisions must be made to hold or gain position, safeguard lives, and minimize damage to colliding boats. A thorough, nay, encyclopedic knowledge of the racing rules is required. Sailboat racers hope fervently that this presentation totally destroys the public's stereotypical image of sailboat racing as an excuse for chubby, out-of-shape people to party, drinks in hand, while drifting around on the water.

"Harold Evonds! Imagine running into you here!"

"John Terman! You old son-of-a-gun! It's been, let's see...two, three years since we've had a chance to talk. How's the wife and family?"

"All's well. thank you. Edith was talking about you and Mary just the other day, wondering why we haven't seen much of you lately. How's little Arnold? Growing like a weed, I suppose."

"Yes, and Katrina. You haven't seen her yet. She's two now, a beautiful child. Here, I'll get my wallet and show you her picture..Mmph! There. Can you reach it? Sorry it got so soaking wet."

"Almost got it. Can you swim a little closer to my boat?"

"Yes, as soon as I free my legs from these lines and climb over the sail. I hope you didn't damage your boat 's bow too badly when you broadsided me."

"No, just a small crack at the starboard-side weld of the pulpit. It did chip about six square inches of gel coat, however. Nasty chip! There, I got the picture. Yes, she's a lovely little girl. Has Mary's eyes, but your smile."

"I'd have dried it off for you, but my towels are all in the storage locker and wet besides. My goodness, she's a tough boat! At the speeds we were making I'd have thought the mast would've buckled. Just look at it. Only a three-square-foot hole at the waterline. Water's filling in fast."

"Is it really that small? I'd heard that line of boats is well constructed. Most others would probably be at the bottom by now. I'll wager it'll take a good five minutes for her to go under at the rate she's sinking. Oh, here's a hand up to my boat. Water must be getting cold by now."

"The water *is* rather cold. But remember, John, that under Rule 56, no person shall board a yacht during a race other than the original crew. If I came aboard, I'm afraid you'd be disqualified from the race. Couldn't do that to a friend. "

"Oh yes. I'd forgotten that rule. Thanks for reminding me. But you'll be protesting me anyway, so what's the difference? After all, you were the privileged boat, being on starboard tack, and I was on port tack. My fault!"

"John, I hardly think you should be blamed. These boats are so quiet under sail that they can sneak up on a person before he knows they're there. Now, if you had been watching out and we'd collided, I might have protested. And I should have shouted a warning to you. Besides, I still might be able to get the pump operating and finish the race. We were so far ahead of everyone else, we're still leading."

"Harold, if you're not coming aboard, would you be so kind as to cut your sail and lines away from my boat? Then I'll be on my way to the finish line."

"Certainly. Glad to oblige. Uumph! Uff! Whew! It's difficult swimming around with clothes on. Sorry to be taking so long."

"Please hurry. Les Femmer's boat is only 100 yards away, and he's getting ready to tack for the mark."

"Ha, ha, ha, ha! He'll have a hard time finding it. Your boat ricocheted into it and sank it when we collided."

"DARN! Oops! Excuse me for swearing. That means I'll

have to sail in a complete circle around where I think it was, before continuing on. They just don't make marks like they once did. No pride in workmanship."

"Whoa! There goes my boat to the bottom! Too late to race now. Drats! All I needed was a third place finish today to cinch the series trophy. John, why not use me as the mark for your circle? I might as well be of *some* use while I'm here in the water."

"Thanks, Harold, I will. Sorry about your boat. She was a beauty. OOPS! Sorry to hit you. Are you okay?"

"Think so. Appears to be only a simple rib fracture and a few abrasions. You'd better hurry. Les is closing fast."

"There, I'm clear. I'll try to hail a power boat to pick you up. If I don't see one, it's only a half-mile swim to the beach. Here, I'll throw you a life jacket."

"John, NO! Remember the rules. While racing, a boat must finish with the equipment with which it started the race, otherwise a disqualification. I'll swim as I am for shore. When you dock, would you call Mary and ask her if she could possibly pick me up there at the park?"

"Will do. Before I forget, I got a hot stock tip this morning. Buy all you can of Esmelta Mining. It's bound to triple by the year's end. Good to see you again, Harold."

"Thanks for the tip. Good luck. Give my best to Edith."

Author's Note: My proofreader, after finishing this story, agreed that most of the racing conversations she's heard while racing are gentlemanly or ladylike, following the example you've just read. However, she claimed, and was backed up by the editor, a one-time sailboat racer himself, that while crewing during a race, he once heard a conversation at a mark that went more along these lines:

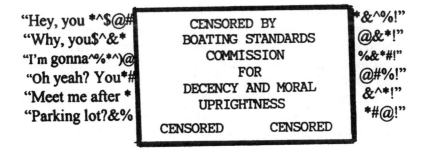

"Hey, you *^$@#   &^%!"
"Why, you$^&*   @&*!"
"I'm gonna^%*^)@   %&*#!"
"Oh yeah? You*#   @#%!"
"Meet me after *   &^*!"
"Parking lot?&%   *#@!"

CENSORED BY
BOATING STANDARDS
COMMISSION
FOR
DECENCY AND MORAL
UPRIGHTNESS

CENSORED   CENSORED

I shushed them, realizing that what they had heard wasn't likely to occur again in this century. Unfortunately, one of the printers contacted a friend of his, chairman of the Boating Standards Commission, who arrived at the print shop with his ilk, all armed with crowbars, sledgehammers, and axes. After breaking down the door of the shop and bullying the assembled workers and author around, he placed his own official censor's stamp on the alleged conversation, thus depriving you, the reader, of the full flavor of the other side of the conversational coin. It is hoped this does not presage the rise of road rage's ugly cousin, race boat rage.

A TUNELESS WHISTLE

It was truly no surprise when the International America's Cup Rules Committee decided to abandon the match-racing format and return to the fleet racing that had originally sparked the Cup competition. Match racing that involved only two boats racing head-to-head had evolved into an innovative, high-tech, expensive venture for boat sponsors. It had eliminated most countries of the world that would have liked to race, and added a layer of elite snobbishness to the whole affair. There were advantages gained, of course, gained through the research and development teams, ever searching for stronger and faster designs and materials, improved and longer lasting sailcloth, hull, and keel improvements, adding speed and stability, and sturdier equipment, all of which gradually filtered down to the average boating enthusiast, undeniably adding to greater safety and pleasure.

The competing yachts' construction still had to abide by a complicated formula, including boat length, beam width, sail area, total weight, and a host of other details that would tend to equalize each boat's chances of winning the Cup. But the return to the original format would once again give the world one of sport's most majestic sights, a fleet of colorful, graceful boats maneuvering dangerously at the starting line. The change had been made so suddenly that only 35 countries had had time to develop and construct a boat in time for the competition. The race committee was immensely relieved at the number, because with some 240 countries in the world, they had envisioned a total nightmare of colliding boats, and protests at the start of each race.

Each country, as usual, worked in total secrecy, jealously guarding against another country's spies stealing some winning-edge idea. Let's go down to the docks and look behind the scenes at the American team's final brainstorming session before the races. There are to be five, each roughly 120 miles in length, with three turning buoys on the course. The *General George Washington*, America's entry, lies veiled under heavy guard at its moorage. A team of four scuba divers patrols underwater to keep competitors from sneaking a peek at a new keel design hinted at in the newspapers. The total team: sponsors, sailmakers, construction team, provisioners, crew, trainers, and meteorologists is in the war room at the U.S. Sail Head-quarters.

"Gentlemen, we must leave nothing to chance. The honor of our country is at stake. International prestige demands our defending and winning the Cup against the rest of the world. This is our final meeting. Are there any final thoughts or questions that might be a key to our having overlooked any detail whatsoever?"

The men in the room, each specialists and experts in their own fields, consulted their notebooks and printout sheets. No one spoke or raised a hand. No stone had been left unturned to ensure a victory.

Fred Furnier, syndicate chairman, spoke again. "Then let's have a final summary. Mr. Calkins, hull and keel."

"I'm glad to report there've been no final changes needed. No restrictions to water flow along the hull. Our round-the-clock underwater guards have fended off all incursions and forays by com-petitors. The keel design will be a complete surprise to them. We must ensure, though, that the hull and keel are cleaned to perfection after each race's haulout. We could use two more scrubbers. Probably run another $3,000 for men and materials."

"Granted. Hire them immediately, and purchase all supplies necessary. Mr. Gouden, sail report." Furnier smiled broadly as Craig Gouden approached the microphone. "Some of you here may not yet have heard of our breakthrough in sail design. It's computer designed, and quite frankly, unbelievable in concept. We've kept it hushed up till now to prevent the idea from falling into our competitors' hands. Mr. Gouden developed and ramrodded the project. Craig, please explain in as much non-technical detail as possible, so the major points are covered."

Craig Gouden, characterized and ridiculed by all as the com-plete computer nerd, glanced confidently around the room. He was about to be named "Boating Industry's Innovator of the Year," and, in sailing circles, gloried in the knowledge that his name would live forever wherever sailors gathered. He began.

"Our top-secret cloth has been named 'Gouden Flowthrough Sailcloth.' I happily report that it has worked 100% perfectly during sea trials under every wind condition. The trials were held at another site to prevent tipping our hand to our competitors. We all know that a sailboat sails at its best and fastest while tacking to windward, at a certain angle of heel. The cloth is a special weave, with sensors sewn in every half-inch over the entire sail that determine wind velocity. The sensors are calibrated for each boat individually, and open or close tiny openings in the sails to keep the boat at its optimum angle of heel. Nobody aboard the boat has to do a thing to adjust the sensors. It's automatic, built in, and will never wear out.

The implications to you are obvious. No more having to waste time making sail changes or reefing the mains'l. The boat, consequently, *never has to lose speed by having to change sails!* We will keep moving constantly at the boat's rated best speed for the wind condition it's in. We compute a savings of six to ten minutes per mile sailed, depending on wind speed. Our backup sails are in place, and as far as sails go, we're ready to take on the world!"

There was a total silence in the room. As the full significance of his remarks sank in, the men leaped to their feet, cheering and clapping. There was no way the *General George Washington* could lose! Two of the larger men ran forward, hoisted Gouden to their shoulders, and ran around the room, the other men pounding Gouden as he passed by.

"Great work, Mr. Gouden! Mr. Clarke, deck equipment, halyards, and lines. Report, please."
"We made the breakthrough in vanadium-rubidium shrouds, stays, mast and boom, rudder, winches and deck fittings, thanks mainly to your $3,000,000 research grant, Mr. Furnier. There is NO possibility of ANY metallic stress failure anywhere on the boat. All lines, formerly made of synthetic materials, have been engineered

with a variation of Mr. Gouden's sailcloth material, without the sensors, and are guaranteed against breakage or failure of any kind."

"Love that report. Good work. Mr. Alerman, crew selection, training, and progress."

Will Alerman, venerable taskmaster for National Crew Development, Inc., took the floor. "We have fourteen of our country's best, strongest, quickest, intelligent, and dedicated young men as crew. They're experienced sailors, have trained for over a year together, and think as one. Because you moved their families here and bought homes for them, their morale is high. They do express concern for their futures after the races are over. Is it at all possible they'll be able to secure employment with you after the races?"

"Of course. Furnier Industries is expanding worldwide. There will be opportunities in sales and management. We'll start all you crew men at, say, $65,000 a year with a company car for personal use. Mr. Alerman, you've done an admirable job training these young men. Mr. Collins, let's have your meteorological reports for the next three weeks. The only thing I fear is light winds during the competition."

"We've micro-analyzed the race area's temperature and wind variations for the past 30 years. We can predict with 96% accuracy the wind velocity at any time of the day, the temperature hour by hour, and the tidal direction and current speed anywhere on the course minute by minute. We can locate wind shifts before they occur, and we're hooked up with the boat's tactician by radio to transmit this information instantly. I foresee no problems."

"Well done. But I'd feel better if you could contact NASA today and see if they can get a weather satellite placed directly over the course with closed-circuit telemetry. I'll authorize a $3,500,000 payment to them now. They can bill me directly later if it's more than that. I really don't know what satellites are going for today."

"Yessir, I'm on it!" Collins leaped from his chair and sprinted from the room. He opened the door so unexpectedly and so forcefully that he nearly knocked down the old custodian, who was dutifully sweeping the hallway. Collins apologized and ran to the communication room.

Furnier was beaming, as was every man in the room. It was going to be over before it started! "Gentlemen, this is the finest team ever assembled! There's *nothing* standing in the way of victory!" Cheering and clapping followed his speech, and backs were pounded. High fives sounded throughout the room as the men celebrated.

"Notting, Mr. Furnier?" The voice, soft and mossy with age, wafted across the room.

"What? Who are you? We're having a meeting here."

"Ay'm Hjalmer Tormson, de coostodian here. Und Ay knows de vun ting you needs to vin de Cup dat you, or non uf de syndicate here, haff efen to't uf, effer."

"You? What do you know about sailing? Please close the door on your way out. Thank you."

The old man stood resolute, without moving, then stepped deeper into the room. "Mr. Furnier, listen to me." His voice crackled with authority this time. His stooped back straightened as he stepped into the circle of men. "As baby, in Norvay, Ay teethed on boat tiller. Ay've sailed effrey boat known to man before you vas effen born, any uf you here. Ay haff Viking blood in me, und Ay haff a secret passed on to me from my vater, who got it from his vater, who got it from his vater, und so on. But Ay luffs dis country now. Becoss Ay'm old now und vill soon be gone Ay'll tell you now de secret. It don' matter ef dis gats out of Viking hands, as dey don' seem to be a fery actife group today. By Odin, haff you seen dere entry fer de Cup race? It look lak Leif Ericsson's longboat ven he discoffered America. Ay can't beliefe it! Leif vould be proud of dem."

As he spoke his voice grew stronger. His pale blue eyes glinted, and the men in the room could almost see him, broadsword and shield in hand, commanding a raiding party along England's coastline. Even Furnier was captured by the mood the old man cast upon all in the room.

"Vot hoppens ven de vind dies? Or yoost blows in gusts un den goes avay und comes und goes?"

All responded, almost to a man. "The boat slows or stops."

"Exactly! Bot vot hoppens ven vun boat, ours, keeps moofing?

129

Und faster und faster?" There was no answer this time. "Ay'll tall you vot, den. As long as *our* boat keeps moofing, it finish, und vins." He grimaced as a spasm of pain danced briefly across his face.

"Now Hjalmer, how can the wind blow for one boat and not another? That's impossible!" Furnier rolled his eyes, while snickers were heard throughout the room.

"Mr. Furnier, Ay vill tall you." His voice lowered. The group leaned in unison towards him. "Da secret...Ef you vistle a toonless vistle, a breeze vill spring op around you und moof de boat. Bot yoost de boat vere vistling come from."

The room exploded with laughter. The old man was crazy after all. Furnier had had enough. He rose, took Hjalmer firmly by the arm, and started to escort him to the door.

"Hjalmer, goodbye. We are really busy today. Thanks a lot for your input. We really appreciate it."

"VAIT! Ay vill proof it! How you tink Leif discoffered dis new place, America? Toonless vistle! Ay svear it troo!" He wrenched away from Furnier, ran to the microphone, and climbed up onto a chair so all could see. He panted from the unaccustomed exertion, but pursed his lips and blew.

A high, soft whistle sounded, then louder, then softer again, followed by trills and arpeggios, softer, louder, but never in a sequence that resembled a tune or melody. Yet, as random as it seemed, there was a certain beauty, an enchantment, that erased the men's laughter. They listened in wonder and awe.

At the desk closest to Hjalmer, a paper stirred. Then another. At desks throughout the room papers began lifting and fluttering helter-skelter to the floor. Computer paper began unfolding, and neckties flew backwards onto shoulders. Hjalmer increased the tempo and volume, causing hair to fly wildly on heads. Those wearing hairpieces grabbed at them as they flew off, their owners becoming believers in the power of the ancient one's tale. Then, as suddenly as he had started, he stopped. Papers that had been flying about dropped to the floor. Combs came out of pockets. Hjalmer surveyed the wild commotion and smiled knowingly. The entire group, Furnier included, sat quietly once more, stunned by the demonstration.

Furnier reacted first. "A tape recorder, quick! Anyone here have a VCR handy? We must have that vistle...er, whistle. Hjalmer, can you show us again?"

"Not a toon, Mr. Furnier, a toonless vistle. Dat's de secret."

"All right! Tuneless! Can you show us again?"

"Ya shoor. Ay can teach you und de crew. Ve haff a veek until de races. It vould be some help ef ve haff some uf de crew be Norvegian or haff some Viking blood in dem. Dose kinds uf guys take to it batter dan anyvun."

A VCR was located and set up. All eyes were on Hjalmer, as if the race depended upon ancient Viking lore, not on the most modern technology available to man. He pursed his lips and blew a soft trill that swelled in volume. Paper began rustling, and men felt their hair beginning to blow about from this magical sound. Hjalmer stopped...put his hands to his head. He groaned, put out his hand to Furnier, and slumped to the floor. Dr. Boehler, syndicate physician, rushed forward to begin first aid, suspecting a possible stroke. Craig Gouden raced to the phone to dial 911 for an ambulance. It arrived within a few minutes, lights flashing, siren wailing. Medics worked on Hjalmer all the way down the stairs and to the ambulance. The group sat once again, shaken by the events of the day.

Furnier, as usual, acted first. "Anyone remember how that sounded? Let's go back to our cubicles, turn on tape recorders, and whistle. Keep a sheet of paper on your desk, and if it starts moving, call me."

The phone call from the hospital was of the good news/bad news sort. It had been a stroke, Hjalmer would live and partially recover enough to walk, but with paralyzed facial muscles, would never whistle again. Furnier was sitting dejectedly at his desk, formulating a plan, when Dan Elyson, foredeck crew chief, burst out of his cubicle, shouting, "I've got it! The paper on my desk moved!" He turned up the volume on his recorder so the others, crowding around, could hear. After eight or ten measures, some of the men thought they'd detected a small breeze, but others weren't sure. Dan turned up the volume more, but Furnier interrupted.

"Dan, it follows Hjalmer's formula, all right, but wait! You knothead! That's our national anthem! I know you're on the right track, but don't use *that!* We don't want any criticism by using it, even to make the boat go. Back to work men, and keep all thoughts of good music out of your heads. At least Dan's tune gives us a start that we know that we can do it, but we need enough force to fill a spinnaker, not just a piece of paper. Clarke, you call everyone in the phone book with a Norwegian-sounding name to see if they have any old-timers around who might know about this. Mason, you call Professor Puccinio, head of the music department at the university. Have him come over with several of his worst students to see if they can help. There might be a lot of modern music that might fill the bill for us. I'll call my psychiatrist to come over to put all who heard Hjalmer under hypnosis to see if we can get an accurate recall on his vistling...er, whistling."

"Hey, everyone, come out onto the deck," shouted Mel Fuerster, crew tactician and helmsman.

They came, and peered down towards the docks where Mel was pointing. Several trucks carrying competing nations' boats had arrived. They awaited their turns at the slings, where boats met water again after long voyages on ocean freighters. A dhow from Egypt was already afloat and being towed to its moorage. The Chinese entry, a beautifully carved teak junk, hung on the sling, and the Canadian entry, a lengthy, cedar-log sailing canoe, lay next in turn, its growly-mouthed, carved, bear prow appearing ready to devour the unwary. The Venezuelan entry, a tightly woven reed boat from the shores of Lake Maracaibo, completed the dock traffic for the moment. The Norwegian entry, having arrived the previous day, lay bobbing in the gentle swells at its moorage, its tall, dragon's head prow staring fiercely seaward.

"Oh, Lord, these new race rules," growled Furnier, shaking his head sadly. "There'll be another thirty boats in tomorrow. I can't believe what *they'll* look like. But men, don't get overly confident by their looks. They may look old fashioned, but they can move. Our spies...er...intelligence agents report that all of them have innovative work on the underwater parts of their hulls. Even the reed boat is modern under water. The woven reeds are just a nationalistic touch. Let's get back to work on that whistle. It's our ace in the hole." And shortly afterwards, each cubicle was filled with the whistling sounds of racers determined to overlook no opportunity to win and keep the Cup.

Race Day. Furnier and his advisers stood easily in their power launch, some 200 yards in back of the racers maneuvering near the starting line. Thirty-four other launches, manned by their syndicate owners and advisors, created as much a traffic jam as the contestants on the starting line were experiencing. The radio crackled. "Mr. Furnier, Mel here. Winds are light but enough to move boats. I swear the Norwegian boat has walrus-hide sails, and that Canadian log is quick. We are in excellent position for the start. Satellite pictures show wind streaks out about a mile. Wish us luck."

At the sound of the starting cannon, the race changed immediately from a wild melee of maneuvering, seemingly erratic boats, to a picture-perfect, military alignment of boats determined to gain a starting edge. It was beautiful! Hearts pounded, and even a few tears coursed down cheeks. Hulls knifing smartly through the ocean swells, they started for their windward turning buoy, some 25 miles upwind. TV crews in planes and helicopters recorded the colorful procession, following them until they were out of sight of shore.

"Jim Nolsen, viewers, here for USBC-TV. We're on the docks at the marina, reporting on the first day's race results. It's an ideal day, clear skies, and winds ranging from three to fourteen knots. Overhead shots show no protest flags flying, so it was all fair and square sailing on this first day of fleet racing. The lighter winds didn't seem to bother the Norwegians in their replica of Leif Ericsson's longboat.
They won handily, after the American boat fell back in the light winds at the north portion of the course, winning by about a

quarter mile. Many experts here today feel the walrus-hide sails of the Norwegian crew gave them some advantage, but whenever the wind picked up, the American boat would close the gap to only 50 yards in some places. This usually occurred when the Norwegians were making sail changes.

The Americans made none, strangely, in a race like this. And what a high-spirited crew the Norwegians have! And musical! They were whistling all the way around the course, as was the American crew when the wind lightened. No one here believes it was their national anthem, but at the same time no one could name the tunes they whistled. It was strange how the two crews distanced themselves from the rest of the fleet. The third-place boat, the Chinese junk, nosed out the Canadian log by fifteen feet, but they and the rest of the fleet were a mile back and closely bunched at the finish. Two more races coming up next week. Now for interviews with the crew of the winning Norwegian longboat. Stay with us as we cover the complete finishing results of the race following the interviews. Back after this word..."

Hjalmer Tormson, watching the race coverage from his hospital bed, saw the results with mixed emotions. His adopted country had not won. His native land had won. There was, then, *still* some ancient Viking knowledge coursing through the veins of these young Norskes. Lore, as he had suspected, had defeated technology. He thought that if Mr. Furnier had been able to find some old-timers who could teach the American crew, the race would've been much closer. For just a brief moment, if someone had been looking at Hjalmer, that someone would have seen a slight change of expression on the old Viking's face. It may have been only one's imagination, but he appeared to be smiling.

LUFF UP, LUFF UP FOR ALMA MATER

News Item: Collegiate sailboat racing is one of the fastest-growing competitive sports today.

"Jim Nolsen here, sports fans, with a first in viewing, USBC-TV's first telecast of a major college sailing regatta. I'll be interviewing Elmore 'Tacks' Broadreach, coach of the Lamprey sailing varsity. They go up against State U's powerhouse Sharks in a regatta to decide the conference championship. Tacks, how do things look for the Lampries?"

"Not too bad, Jim. It should be a good match-up. We're both 8-0 this season. We've got solid sailors of every weight class in nearly every boat to match the wind conditions. We have a good balance of senior leadership and a promising underclass. Only our #4 boat lacks an outstanding light-air skipper, unfortunately."

"I don't understand what you mean, Tacks. Could you explain to our millions of viewers?"

"Yes. Simply that in light winds we sail a 125-pound lad, in medium winds a 150-pounder, and in heavy airs above 18 knots, we sail our 200-pounders to keep the boat from capsizing, and these 16' boats can and *will,* if mishandled."

"Got it. But what happens if a lightweight skipper gets caught in, let's say, 30-knot winds?"

"That happened to us earlier this season against the Dog-fish, in a race right here on the lake. It was murder! The wind came out of nowhere and hit so fast and hard that the lads weren't able to lean back and dip their sweatshirts into the water in time to add weight and keep their boats up. Boats turned turtle everywhere. Poor Jurgen Heigmichtor, an all-conference skipper, drowned, and has gone to that great luffing match in the sky."

"Wasn't he wearing a life jacket?"

"Yes he was, Jim, but under it he was wearing seven sweatshirts and a lead belt to increase boat stability. When the wind hit, he swerved to avoid a collision, capsized, and went down like a rock. The lead belt overcame the buoyancy of the life jacket."

"How awful, Tacks. What did you do?"

"Well, we protested, of course. After all, he was on starboard tack and had the right-of-way. We won the protest, too, I might add."

"No, I mean what did you do about poor Jurgen?"

"We dragged for him after the regatta, naturally. But the lake's so deep where he went down it's doubtful we'll find him, with that lead belt on."

"Is that all you did?"

"Of course not, Jim. The Board of Regents is considering naming one of our boats after him. Maybe, if we can get the alumni sailing group involved, even the boathouse."

"No, no, Tacks. What I really meant to say was, are the other team members taking proper precautions now, such as eliminating the extra sweatshirts and lead belts?"

"No way, Jim. All the schools sail that way. If we didn't, we'd lose all our races. Gotta keep those boats up! Jim, you don't want the alumni on my back, do you?"

"Sorry, Tacks, I didn't think of *that*. But except for that terrible mishap, the rest of the team's in good shape?"

"No, we're hurting in the #7 and #8 boats. Two of our better sailors are in the campus infirmary with sprained vocal cords. Can't sail competitively without the voice box in good shape. It's just part of competitive sailing."

"That's unusual, Tacks. What happened?"

"If you'd ever done any sailboat racing you'd know there's an awful lot of yelling at each other during the race, especially at the buoys, where things get really hairy at times. You should have an opportunity to hear them yell! Whew!"

"What do they yell?"

"Generally warnings to other boats, rules interpretations, or just cussing at each other, like football players do. I can't tell you more specifically because I don't understand German or Swedish."

"Tacks, that brings up another point. I notice on the team roster that many of the names have a foreign flavor. Heinreich Schiemann, Klaus Schmidten, Pero Benngsston, Waldemar Gauseflesch, and Igor Boroskovsky, for example. Are those American boys?"

"No, they're transfer students from Europe on our sailing scholarships. Sailing is far more advanced at the junior level over there, so we recruit heavily in Germany, Norway, Sweden, Italy, and Spain. In fact, I recruited the entire championship team from Schnellschiff High School in Umlaut, Germany this year. We'll be highly competitive in the next few years. Should be in the Final Four."

"Isn't that unfair to the young American sailors who'd like to compete for you here as a Lamprey?"

"Jim, we borrowed the idea from the college football and basketball coaches. They bring in seven-footers from Africa and Europe to play ball here, and track coaches recruit heavily in Africa. The villagers there grow very fleet of foot trying to escape elephant charges and hungry lion attacks and such. Just look at the Olympic gold medalists in track. Many are from African countries."

"I see what you mean, Tacks. I've heard that watching a sailing regatta is a lot like watching grass grow. Yet I see hundreds of spectators in the stands today, all college students and all young men. What's the explanation?"

"Take care what you say, Jim. Watching grass grow is one of our best training exercises. Every day, for the first 15 minutes of practice, we sit here on the lawn and watch grass grow. It's great for keeping them in shape mentally. You see, after watching the grass grow, moving along in light winds at half-a-knot seems comparatively exciting."

"I can certainly agree with you on that. Viewers, we've arrived at the varsity boathouse, where we'll listen to Tacks give his pep talk and final instructions to the team and...GOOD HEAVENS!...I MEAN, WOW! TACKS! WHO'S THAT SENSATIONAL YOUNG LADY? HOW CAN SHE...Sorry, viewers...Tacks, how can she stay warm today dressed like THAT?"

"Easy, Jim. That's OOly La Coorve, our cheerleading queen. She and the pep staff come to the regatta to help inspire the team. Skipper of the boat with the largest winning margin gets to take her out on a date, chaperoned, however, by the Dean of Women. Average boat speed has increased by 1.37 knots, and even on windless days our boys manage to keep the boats moving somehow. Probably from hard breathing thinking about OOly. We owe a lot of our success this year to her. We have to dress her and the rest of the girls on the pep staff like that or the team's concentration will be broken by watching the girls that go by on some of those big powerboats. We also found that with our pep staff and cheerleaders in action, we've increased attendance from three or four fans to 1,200-1,500 per regatta. With the minimal $.50 admission charge for seating, the sailing program here is self-sustaining."

"Tacks, I can certainly understand why. But I get the idea that the guys are here to watch the girls lead cheers and dance, rather than watch the races."

"I wouldn't be surprised, but that's their choice. Besides, being on shore, they can't see much of the race action after the boats get farther out on the lake. Mostly starts and finishes are what they are interested in anyway."

"Here we are now, at lakeside on the dock. A four-to-five-knot breeze is ruffling the sails on the boats. Tacks has gathered his varsity for the pep talk and last-minute instructions. While you're listening to Tacks, I'll take a few minutes to interview OOly La Coorve, to...to...to get the women's perspective on sailing and her role in the success of the Lamprey team this year. Here's Tacks..."

"Okay, team this is it! The big one for all the marbles. It's hard to be first in anything, but you've got your chances now, today! We've got to get it all together to beat State. Minimize mistakes. Cover the open boat. Control your luff. Go for the long tack. Out-4th-leg them. If they capsize, drive hard for the next mark. Remember OOly! You freshmen! Remember that the spinnaker, while theoretically pulling the boat along faster while wrapped around the forestay, actually makes the boat go faster if allowed to assume a more fully rounded shape clear of and ahead of the forestay. You sophomores! Tank testing has conclusively proved that any sail dragging in the water has very little, if any, effect on moving the boat faster!

Let's bow our heads for a moment for our dear, departed teammate. I know Jurgen is out there somewhere, watching you and hoping you can win for him. Incidentally, if you see him surface, you might throw out a fender in the vicinity. All of you! Remember. There may be wind today from the north, south, east or west. Or some other direction, like southeast or northwest. Maybe even south by southeast or northwest by north. If it's not moving your boat, it's probably not blowing at all. It may be blowing inshore or offshore. If you don't have it, go elsewhere to get it. Find a way! But no paddling! Avoid holes, those dead spots on the water where the wind's not blowing. They're easy to locate. If you're not moving, you're already *in* one. Now go out there and let's see a Lamprey win today!"

"Jim Nolsen, here, once again. What a wild scene! The spectators are on their feet, waving the Lamprey blue-and-green pennants and cheering wildly. The pep staff and cheer leaders, led by OOly, are dancing on the beach. As the varsity team members raise sails, they're screaming, 'GO, GO, GO LAMPREY TEAM, GO!' There you have it, viewers. We'll be back for the starting gun and an interview with OOly La Coorve, right after this short message from our sponsors."

SAILING CLASSICS ONCE RETOLD - I
A World Championship

Event: Pacific Coast Single-Handed Championship Race
Place: Puget Sound, State of Washington
Boats: Sea Witch Class, 20' LOA (Length Over All)
Winds: 0 knots, much of race, to 14 knots
Tides: Flood at 3.1 knots, Ebb at 2.1 knots
Ron Denston, Los Angeles, vs. Chuck Gerlind, Seattle

For most men to come even *close* to a world record in *any* competitive event would be thrill enough to provide enough memories for a lifetime. Little did Chuck Gerlind dream that by the end of today's race final he would smash *three* existing records, yet in winds that would leave his sails limp most of the day, and leave him without the exhilaration that traditionally accompanies victory and setting of records. In Chuck's case, *all three* would be *world* records!

It looked like it would be over at the start, as Denston, coming about hard on his final drive to the starting line, snapped his boat's tiller off at its base. Using his ingenuity quickly, he fitted a 12-inch monkey wrench onto the post to use during the race. Even so, the boats were only 15 seconds apart when the wind began to slacken. Many race experts, upon post-race analysis, felt the turning point of the race came when a superferry on a regular run passed between the two boats. Its huge bulk totally blanketed Gerlind, stopping him completely.

Denston, barely able to clear the gigantic ferry, was caught in its stern "jet stream" and was sucked along backwards at 16 knots to the Kingston buoy, the first turning mark on the course, where the ferry slowed on its approach to the Kingston terminal. Ferry Captain Sven Berg was later quoted as " I took my boat full speed across the Sound. I wasn't going to let a limp-sailed ragboat beat the state's newest, fastest superferry across. I'd a-been laughed right out of the service!"

Denston, being from out of state, did not have good local knowledge of the waters. Mistaking a large flyspeck on his charts for the second buoy, he set sail on a course that, while legal, took him two miles out of his way. By luck, it brought him into the only patch of wind on the entire course, and he soon sailed out of sight of Gerlind. Gerlind, with no wind to drive his boat, found the current had carried his boat into a thick, 15-acre bed of kelp. He spent nearly an hour disentangling himself from it, nearly becoming asphyxiated by the exhaust smoke from three large tugboats hauling loaded barges down the sound.

Denston finished the race, showered, accepted the winner's trophy following a banquet at the clubhouse, and came back from a late date at 10:00 P.M., late for *him*, not so late for other sailors, who, being people who live clean lives, tend to get back before midnight, as a rule. All this occurred before Gerlind was able to rudder-scull the three miles back to the clubhouse dock against a 2.5 flood tide, arriving back around 10:30 P.M., angry and exhausted.

The records are very clear, and have been sent away for official verification and authentication. Dr. Gene Warken, leaving the clubhouse with two colleagues, noted Gerlind's bright red face and insane muttering as he pulled himself onto the dock from his boat. Suspecting a possible coronary, Dr. Warken pulled a sphygmomanometer from his case, measuring Gerlind at 395(systolic)/346(diastolic), with a pulse rate of 327 beats per minute, all world records, pending official verification. However, with two medical doctors as witnesses to this event, it seems only a matter of time before the figures are accepted as legitimate.

Note: The systolic record has recently been tied by Sir Malcom Littleton-Smythehurst, world-renowned big game hunter. After following a trophy-sized leopard to the 17,000-foot level of Mt. Kilimanjaro, he asked Ngabwa Yunswafasi, his gun bearer, for the rifle. Ngabwa, thinking several hours back that Sir Malcom would soon stop climbing due to the heat of the day, replied that he had left it at the 4,000-foot level. Both Chuck Gerlind and Sir Malcom recovered fully, although Sir Malcom lay in a state of shock for three days after his opportunity for his world record had escaped.

SAILING CLASSICS ONCE RETOLD - II
A European Championship Race

Event: European Championships - Final Race
Place: Nach-um-Baden Yacht Club, Vorfjord, Sweden
Boats: Open classification, 18' maximum LOA
Winds: 8-12 knots
Tides and currents: Negligible

Europe's most memorable match was dueled in sparkling waters after the grueling preliminaries had eliminated nearly 200 hopefuls. The final race pitted the boat sponsors, business rivals Asle Bodten, the Swedish wine king, against Pieter Mull-Genst, German 8-Neider magnate. (In America we would say 8-Down. It is a noncarbonated light beer, felt by most Americans to be slightly bitter, although no lost traveler on the Sahara Desert, when finally found, has ever been known to say anything negative about it. The name was coined by Mull-Genst himself, after downing eight bottles to prevent dehydration while lost on a sales trip to Timbuktu.)

It had been a regatta series surrounded by controversy from the beginning. Despite being billed as an open event, that is, any boat could initially enter without construction limitations as long as the boat was less than 18 feet in length, Bodten's entry had been found "nonconforming." The entire hull had been designed in the shape of an 18-foot glass wine bottle. It was finally accepted after Bodten agreed to remove the gigantic cork at the bow, a feat that kept his glass-cutting crew busy till 30 minutes before the first race.

Mull-Genst's boat had been initially declined because of its sail plan, thought to be "too commercial," a contention so strong that he was forced to use the more conventional white sails during the entire race. His mains'l had been designed and colored to resemble the distinctive 8-Neider bottle, with a small gaff supporting the sail's neck. He had also agreed to return to traditional sail numbers, rather than keep the sail showing an eagle, unicorn, and three hummingbirds

143

wading in the pure spring water from which 8-Neider is allegedly brewed. Both men had agreed to these changes in order to compete. There was much at stake, as the sponsor of the winning boat would gain thousands of converts and new customers to its product, boundless prestige, and *immense* profits.

The race was most notable, however, for the introduction of the now-common psychological ploy, introduced by Nachterwein just moments before the start, of the "Madchen-an-steuerbord-Balken" tactic. This has been much refined since the race, and has been found to be most effective when shouted in a loud voice with eyebrows raised, tongue hanging out, a broad smile, and a look of serious longing.

Nachterwein knew that Hannssen was well known for his *madchen* (girl)-chasing prowess, as well as a serious lack of concentration. (Hannssen had once lured a lovely sailing groupie to his apartment, ostensibly to show her his sailing trophies, only to spend the evening showing her his sailing trophies. Note: Read "A Night Sailing with Sig," or 'Sailing can be Boring," written by Annie Schticknagel, *Treue Liebe Magazine,* May 17, 1999, 137:47-51.)

Hannssen reacted as Nachterwein had hoped, snapping his head to the *steuerbord* (starboard), *balken* (beam, or side), of his boat in his search for a topless, possibly bottomless, beauty. It must be remembered, in all fairness to Hannssen, that in Europe it is not uncommon practice for madchens on both large and small boats to appear "*ausserhalb bluse*"(without tops), or for that matter, "*nackt,*" that is, without *any* clothing at all. In America we would say "naked." In this case, however, Hannssen was completely fooled, as the only boat visible on the steuerbord Balken was a tug hauling a garbage scow to be dumped far out in the Kattegat.

Nachterwein had observed that Hannssen had *some* knowledge of German vocabulary, although quite limited, as he had seen Hannssen pursue a delectable madchen into a room clearly marked, "Frauen Waschenraum."("Ladies Room," in America), only to reappear immediately, accompanied by loud screams from the Waschenraum.

It took Hannssen only 10-15 seconds to realize the garbage scow did not contain the hoped-for view, nor did the tug. The only person aboard was the operator, Kapitan Heinrich Schlimmler, obese, drunken ex-U-boat (U-93), Kommander, who had removed his shirt due to the heat of the day. Upon close or far inspection, he does not resemble a madchen in any way whatsoever, and as far as is known, has never been chased into a waschenraum by anyone, at least not with a right mind.

By the time Hannssen realized he had been cleverly duped by Nachterwein, Hans had tacked to steuerbord himself, received a lift in the clear air, and was never thereafter seriously threatened. The race might have been close, even with Nachterwein's early advantage, had not Hannssen's boat sailed too close to the garbage scow, which was having part of its cargo blown into the water. At liftout after the race, Hannssen's boat was found to have an immense, sodden cardboard furniture carton wrapped around its centerboard.

Some race experts feel this may have created a slight drag, enough to prevent Hannssen's chances of being able to develop the speed necessary to catch and pass Nachterwein and win. There has now developed a wild controversy between different sailing factions in regards to this matter. A mediator has both sides agreeing, at long last, to abide by the results of tank testing model boats, some with nothing on their centerboards, others adorned with various materials wrapped around them. Complete analysis should be completed within six months and will be available to the public—especially boaters, who should know these things.

Hannssen, dismissed immediately by Bodten, an action thought by most to be unfair, considering the matter of the cardboard carton, was soon hired by Mull-Genst, and now sells 8-Neider in the desert areas of the world. Once a sailor, always a sailor. Hannssen claims sailing is not difficult in the deserts. He makes his sales calls in a self-designed, extremely light balsa-and-aluminum boat for sailing in mirages. Many scoff at this claim, believing he has either been out in the heat of the Sahara too long, or is suffering mental deterioration from having drunk too much 8-Neider.

SEX AND THE BOATER

Boating, by its very nature, is at the least, romantic, and at the very best, passionate. Dreams of both male and female boaters, *and* boatless landlubbers, as reported by professional dream analysts, are commonly punctuated with common fantasies, such as those described in the following examples of amorous nighttime visualizations in dream states:

1. A magnificent, always at least 42-foot boat, *never* a rowboat, canoe, runabout, inflatable or small day sailer.
2. On a tropical isle, palm branches wave gently, with a white sand beach reflecting the brilliant glow of a full moon.
3. A soft, warm breeze, rocking the safely anchored craft slightly in the cool, clear sea water.
4. Tiny wavelets drumming melodically against the well-polished hull, always a white one, unless the dream has reverted back to olden times, in which the boat, or ship, in this scenario, assumes the shape of a pirate craft, with Jolly Roger flying aft and 10-24 cannon bristling along the cannon ports, ready to fire in case of attack by the Spanish attempting to get their treasure back.
5. The faint sounds of a large group of local natives singing as they're gathered 'round a glowing beach fire, always on pitch and accompanied by their exotic, in-tune, native musical instruments. A rhythmic, sensual group of drums beating in an unrelenting, hypnotic mode that heightens one's basic instincts and emotions.
6. A wild boar roasting on a spit over the red-hot coals, sending its aromatic odor along the beach. If the dream is of cannibals, a captured enemy replaces the boar on the spit, but the odor, strangely enough, remains the same.
7. For the female dreamer, a handsome, tanned, bulked-up wealthy, intelligent hunk. For the male dreamer, a gorgeous, voluptuous, tanned, smiling, intelligent dream girl, almost always with a charming, intriguing foreign accent and white teeth, which shine as she smiles.
8. The Adonis usually has numerous scars and bandaged wounds received as a result of mysterious activities, such as spying

147

on foreign terrorists, who wear scraggly beards and funny looking hats. He has escaped capture and torture, and has returned to a grateful government with important secrets, but cannot divulge to his paramour his whereabouts during these times because of strict security regulations. If revealed, she would share his extreme jeopardy and danger of being assassinated by those same vengeful enemy terrorists.

9. The dream girl, who has just returned from a conference of world leaders, where *her* plan to save the world from economic collapse has just been wildly acclaimed, is in hiding from foreign leaders, who fear her brilliant plans will keep them from stealing further millions from their countries' treasuries. She has just escaped a wild car chase, had about 800 bullets fired at her, and has fended off an attack by five karate, judo, and jiu jitsu experts hired to bring her to a foreign hideaway in chains, but not a hair is out of place, and she continues to smile, charming all in the dream.

10. Analysts report that dreamers, both male and female, actually *become* these impossibly perfect physical specimens while dreaming. They vicariously participate in all the sensual activities that even those of little imagination could imagine happening as a result of finding themselves in the types of scenes just described. Most men, however, would have trouble explaining scars resulting from merely trying to cross a street in Los Angeles or Seattle during rush hour, or for some, by accidentally nicking themselves with a razor while shaving. The experts also feel Hollywood shares the blame for dreams like these by producing a constant stream of impossibly romantic movies, thereby actually *shaping* the mind by widening the mind's perception of what could possibly happen, usually far outside the limits of what an average person might expect in real life.

So, no rain, beach fleas, smoke-in-the-eyes beach fires, sea sickness, bad-tasting meals, driving wind that musses the hair, moonless nights, boat-capsizing gales, natives singing off-key, bratty children, plugged-up toilets, sunburn, or less-than-perfect people with stained teeth ever appear in Hollywood productions. And no dirty boats with frayed lines, the usual look of a boat after a lengthy cruise, ever appear in a dream, except possibly as a beached hulk in the background. The well-coifed, after a boat has left on a cruise in real life, shortly become wind-blown, with hair assuming a porcupine-like texture, stiff, bristled, and avoiding one's attempts to make it look decent. Indeed, a woman sailor aboard will usually either shave her head or wear a scarf constantly, others on the boat not seeing her hair until returning home, and then only after a severe washing followed by a beauty parlor perm.

Despite all the problems that might occur, boaters have found ways to overcome them to participate, although less frequently than the land-bound, in affairs of the heart. It is not uncommon for them to enjoy the supreme ecstasy of romance aboard. Many are the true tales of a couple departing on, say, a three-year voyage around the world, only to return three years later with an infant in their arms, or a two-year-old toddling off the boat and onto land for the first time, or both, for that matter. Human nature, it appears, will come out wherever humans are found, on land or at sea.

That brings us to the essence of this chapter. Finally, you say. I can hear it from here, above the roar of the waves crashing onto the beach. The *really good* part of the book. Given the usual crowded space aboard most boats, even the largest ones, storms can shake and rattle not only a boat, but the crew and passengers as well. Despite lack of space and storms that rock a boat, plus seasickness, sunburn, and cabin fever, romance will have its way.

The following pages may be considered as a manual for the where-to, when-to, and how-to of that most delightful and powerful activity of the human condition. To include nationalistic practices of boaters world-wide would be to write an encyclopedic set of books. After studying sexual practices throughout the world, I have been able to ascertain that there is a basic, common core of activities and practices everywhere that will be reflected in this chapter, saving you the trouble of lugging a heavy set of books on the subject with you when you go out on a date, or on a honeymoon, or wherever.

There are three places in the world that reflect the highest average of these practices, all three of which I will detail here. Not only are these the best examples, but all three sites are among the most romantic cruising areas known to boaters: The San Juan Islands of Washington State, the numerous islands of the Caribbean, and the scattered islands of the archipelago nations of the South Pacific Ocean.

I know I will receive thousands of letters protesting that the writers of those letters know of more romantic spots, and will send pictures of their numerous children to prove it, but remember that these three sites represent the *average* of the best sexual practices, not the warmest, most scenic, or those having the best anchorages closest to good shopping, the highest number of four-star restaurants, or the areas having the fewest numbers of beach fleas or other objectionable insect life.

BALANCED SHIP

LOVE IN THE SAN JUAN ISLANDS

THIS CHAPTER

CENSORED

BY THE

BOATING STANDARDS

COMMISSION

FOR

DECENCY AND MORAL

UPRIGHTNESS

Anyone reading the pages of this chapter will be liable for a $500 fine and up to 6 months of community service, such as raiding book stores that sell books like this. If assigned this service, please bring your own ax, hammer, sledge hammer and pry bar, mask and gloves. Thank you.

AMOUR IN THE ISLANDS OF THE CARIBBEAN

THIS CHAPTER

CENSORED

BY THE

BOATING STANDARDS

COMMISSION

FOR

DECENCY AND MORAL

UPRIGHTNESS

Anyone reading the pages of *this* chapter will be liable for a $1,000 fine and up to a year of community service. We are watching! Look out!

ROMANCE AS PRACTICED BY BOATERS OF THE SOUTH SEA ISLANDS

THIS CHAPTER

REALLY CENSORED!

BY THE

BOATING STANDARDS

COMMISSION

FOR

DECENCY AND MORAL

UPRIGHTNESS

WHEW!

Anyone reading this chapter is liable to a $5,000 fine and up to 3 years scrubbing graffiti off the walls of public places. On the other hand, go ahead and read it, because we need a lot of graffiti erased off walls.

"...LOOKS LIKE MARGE AND BRAD GOT OVER THEIR LITTLE SPAT..."

THE Y2K PROBLEM: RESOLVED!

The author has taken great pains to ensure that the horrible, catastrophic predictions for 12:00 P.M. on December 31 of 1999, as well as for midnight on *December 31, 2000,* will NOT, repeat, NOT affect this book in any fashion whatsoever! Thanks to the research department at Happy Hills, led by the multitalented Professor Strawbridge and his brilliant assistant, Dr. Jacob Pufmeister, a substance has been developed that will protect this book from any deleterious, mysterious changes in appearance or content.

This new product, named "Page-Fix," is now awaiting assured approval from the U.S. Patent Office. It is invisible, nontoxic, non-allergenic, undetectable on the page, and ensures that *all* letters and numbers printed on a page *will remain fixed in place on the page on both December 31 dates, at the fateful stroke of midnight!* It is also guaranteed that there will be NO FADING of the text for at least the duration of the new millennium, and perhaps the next, as well.

There may well be skeptics and naysayers among the readers, unbelieving that such a product has been developed so successfully, especially at Happy Hills. And so "Page-Fix" will have its detractors. They will simply say, given the powerful forces to be unleashed in Y2K, "It can't be done. It's impossible!" No rational scientific proof backs their claims, offering only the closed-mindedness of those who still refuse to believe that the bumblebee can fly, given its wing-span-to-body mass ratio.

To ease your minds that "Page-Fix" actually works as advertised, and that your copy is safe from danger, the author and publisher have arranged to present to you the *actual unaltered lab-test results, untouched and realistic! Right here, before your very eyes!* You no longer have to accept the word, however truthful, of the test-lab scientists.

Test #1 - Test for word/number page stability. The test area, on plain white paper, has been printed with regular printing ink infused with "Page-Fix." After printout the test area was thoroughly computer tested for any Y2K problem that might occur on December 31 at 12:00 P.M. **Test area #1** just below:

While on a cruise to the San Juan Islands, a boater became totally lost. Most of the islands tend to look alike, rocky beaches, hemmed in by thousands of huge fir trees growing as close together as Mother Nature allows being the usual appearance. Add the impenetrable jungle-like undergrowth of nettles, devil's club, ferns, blackberry bushes, and other miscellaneous plant life attempting to establish itself, plus the usual thick fog, and one can easily see how easy it is to become disoriented.

Indeed, many San Juanites have grown immensely wealthy from rewards given them by grateful lost boaters being found. Others gained wealth by salvaging derelict boats, whose owners, still aboard, had died of starvation. (If they had had a copy this book aboard and read pages 104-110, they'd not have died so needlessly.) During the summer months, college-age San Juanites gather in boats just off Fog Point to rescue lost boaters, much the same as taxicabs gather at the bus depots of larger cities. Many have earned enough to finance college educations and have enough left over to establish themselves in business following graduation, or take extended world cruises. The lost boater mentioned previously, desperate, finally spotted a

---

End of Test #1 - Results: As you can determine easily, simply by observation, the test area passed the print stability test with flying colors. The lines are straight, fixed in place, with no fading or discoloration. This should prove to even the most unbelieving skeptic that "Page-Fix" works reliably!

Test #2 - Test for word stability on plain white paper that has been *untreated* with "Page-Fix."

While on a cruise to the San Juan Islands, a bo
ater became lost. Most of the islands tend to look
alike, a rocky beach, hemmed in by t
thousands of huge fir trees growing together and
as closely as Mother allows
black berrie s
wealth
[illegible]
a simple [illegible]

END OF TEST #2
SUMMARY OF FINDINGS:

The test results are obvious, even to the visually impaired, by a mere glance comparing the two tests. The untreated words have sagged badly, and in many places have actually slid totally down to the bottom of the untreated test area #2. The scientifically-developed test should have no detractors after seeing these results. The test was shortened due to recognition by the scientists that even from the ADJACENT Room, where the Y2K test equipment is located, that the equipment was having an effect, causing sagging and slippage of the printed words on the page.

END OF Y2K REPORT

As you have seen throughout the book, I, the author, have not resorted to bragging about anything. Oh, I have happily presented the accomplishments of others, particularly Prof. Strawbridge and Dr. Pufmeister, astounded as I am by their outstanding work in spite of having only a few test tubes and beakers at hand, and by their limited financial resources, namely R&D money. So I must brag a little about the work of Dr. Pufmeister, who has taken "Page-Fix" a step further by inventing a new product, "Page-Fix+," which is now awaiting federal trademark approval. This + factor ensures that any object treated with it becomes invulnerable to fire up to 1,800 degrees Fahrenheit, as well as protecting against Y2K problems on printed pages. Because the federal approval is still being awaited, only the following chapter, *The World's Most Hilarious Boating Bloopers,* has been treated with "Page-Fix+." Even if your house burns to the ground and the rest of the book is completely incinerated, you will still have the blooper chapter remaining untouched, legible, and readable to give you hours of hilarious enjoyment as you survey the blackened ruins of what was, before the fire, a cozy, well-appointed home.

This is a *major* invention. It should put fire departments out of existence as entire communities are sprayed to stave off demented arsonists. As with other technological advances, for example, fire, the wheel, the automobile, the airplane, pizza pie, nose and tongue rings, the boat, paper money, comic books, the telephone, electricity, the computer, spray hair gel and now "Page-Fix" and "Page-Fix+," wild-eyed detractors have historically slowed down the advance of civilization's most important ideas. Some examples from the past:

1. Fire for cooking: "Yah Moog, the mammoth tastes okay heated up but it's just a fad. REAL men eat their meat raw."
2. The wheel: "Okay, so it rolls downhill, but NO WAY you gonna catch up to it to stop it."
3. The automobile: "Pretty fancy, but get going over 22 miles per hour and the breath'll get sucked right out of your lungs!"
4. The airplane: "If God had wanted humans to fly He'd have given us wings. I know Orville. A flying *bicycle*? C'mon!"
5. The telephone: "So Bell claims he can talk to someone miles away over a *wire*. What a screwball! He must take us all for some kind of idiots!"
6. Electricity: "I saw that damn fool Ben out flying a kite again in the rain and that thunderstorm! He claims there's something called electricity up there, and he's trying to get it to come down *here!* That lightning's gonna *kill* him one of these days, doin' that! Ma, can you

move the candle closer over here so I can read my book? And close the window. The candle's flickerin' something awful. Thanks."

7. The computer: No one's going to get *me* to sit down and stare at a screen all day! The abacus and slide rule were good enough for my granpappy and pappy, and they're good enough for *me!* At least they won't go out when the electricity gets knocked out by lightning!"

8. Spray hair gel: "Ain't gonna catch on! We'll all end up lookin' like those gol-dang game show hosts! Yuck!"

With those past quotes in mind, let's examine the test results recently concluded on "Page-Fix+. There seems a certainty that there will be a huge market for it, with all the profits going to Happy Hills research scientists and labs.

Test #3: The test area just below has been treated with the new substance "Page-Fix+" and heated by an arc-welder's torch for one hour at a temperature of 1,900 degrees Fahrenheit, a much higher temperature than the usual house fire.

———————————————————————————————

Test #3: The boater spotted an old beachcomber and motored inshore as close as he dared without grounding. He called to the old fellow, "Ahoy there, where am I?" The beachcomber looked up, saw the boater, and said, "Can't fool me, young feller. You're right there in that boat. But I can't help. I've been lost here for about four years, after cracking up on those rocks you're about to hit. Better back off! I've been living on beach fleas and sandworms. Maybe you can rescue me, and we can be lost together till we can find someone who knows the islands."

———————————————————————————————

END OF TEST #3
SUMMARY OF FINDINGS:

Results: The page looks normal in every respect. The product, "Page-Fix+," passes every claim made for it. Rub it, and you'll find no smudges on your fingers.

Test #4: A plain white sheet of paper using regular ink. Heated by same welder to same temperature as in Test #3:

END OF TEST #4
NO SUMMARY NEEDED, RESULTS EVIDENT
Commentary: Test #4 was quickly ended to prevent the test lab from catching on fire, as the paper burst into flames upon very first application of torch. Compare Tests #3 and #4.

THE WORLD'S MOST HILARIOUS
BOATING BLOOPERS

Author's Note: This is an apology to the reader(s?) of *Boating-Exposed!* This chapter, which was to have been the book's highlight, fell prey to a series of Happy Hills print shop misfortunes, unparalleled in modern times, if not in all history, going back to the caveman.

Fortunately, the events leading to this disaster were caught on the tape that records the sounds of the antiquated print shop machinery. It quickly alerts the supervisors and workers to the ungodly squeals and rasps of malfunctioning gears, belts and drive shafts so that the machines can be shut down and repairs made before the particular machine rips itself apart. The tape also records the conversations of the workers on the floor, hence this reconstruction of events.

I include all this so you'll know for certain that it was *not my fault*, exactly, having left definite, clear, simple, and to-the-point instructions with the print shop personnel. There were only *two* requests, one being that this chapter be printed using "Page-Fix+" in the ink, and the other being that no one should read a fully printed blooper, the ensuing laughter causing a printing slowdown, and we were facing a deadline. However, people are people, even here at Happy Hills. I have had the tape transcribed for you here so you can see for yourself who the culprits were who deprived you of the many humorous events that occur in boating.

The workers in this reconstruction are as follows:
Vern - "The Chief;" print shop supervisor
Arkey - print shop ramrod; Vern's second-in-command
Chuck - shop assistant, flunky, gofer, and cleanup specialist
Slim -shop assistant, flunky, gofer, and cleanup specialist
Inky - ink shop supervisor
Gordon - new man on the job

"Chuck! You and Slim come here. Got a job for you."

"Okay, Chief, what is it?"

"The boys on setup have the plates ready for printing. Chuck, you take the plates down to Bjarne in printing. These plates are the final chapter in the boating book we're finally going to be able to print. They're heavy. Better make three trips, and *be careful!* Don't drop them, 'cause they'll break! Slim, here's our printout on paper, plus the author's original manuscript. Bring both to Annie for archives storage. Then, both of you sweep up around the shredder. I've gotta run."

"Gotcha, Chief." They waited until Vern had gone. "Ya know, Slim, these plates don't look so heavy. Think I'll just take the whole stack at once to save time."

"Chuck, all I've got are these few papers. Here, let me take three of the plates to lighten your load. Ooh! They're heavy, heavier than I thought. Your stack must weigh 70 pounds or so. Maybe better you make three trips."

"I'll handle 'em. Let's go."

The two strode towards the printers' area, stopping once so Chuck could adjust his grip on the slippery stack of plates. The site at which they stopped lay outside the room where several men, clad in white lab coats, were diligently working at computer stations, taking notes on their work as they went.

"Chuck, who are all these new guys, anyway?"

"Vern told me they're running tests to see if Y2K and the following year will affect print shop operations. They're running all sorts of tests on some new product, too, that Professor Strawbridge and Dr. Pufmeister have developed. Got my grip back. Let's move on."

Slim, having one arm relatively free, began swatting at small, black, floating "things" appearing suddenly, settling on their heads, shoulders, arms, and clothing.

"Slim, what are those things? Bugs? I've never seen any-thing like 'em."

"Here, I caught some....They're not bugs. Chuck, looks like...no, it couldn't be...looks like little black d's, b's, p's, and a q. Same size as the manuscript print."

"Slim, you're crazy! Here. Hold your hand out to me so I can see. OOOPS!" As Chuck leaned over to examine the objects in Slim's hand, the top plate slipped off the stack. As it did so, Chuck, in an entirely reflexive move, tried to catch it, resulting in, as one might suspect, the entire stack crashing to the cement floor with a deafening clatter. Bits and pieces flew like shrapnel from an exploding artillery shell. Nearby workers ducked away behind any protection they could find. The two stood dumbfounded.

"Chuck! Here, take my plates! I'll run and get a broom and a waste can." He thrust them at Chuck in such haste that they, too, crashed to the floor, with the same result as the others, smashed to smithereens. The noise and yelling drew the attention of Arkey. His anger was surpassed only by his dismay as he surveyed the scene.

"You idiots! Now look what you've done!" (He always said that when something went wrong, as though the perpetrators couldn't have seen what they had just wrought.)

We can assume, correctly, that Chuck and Slim had already seen what they'd done, first to see, in fact. "Slim! What are all those little specks on you? They're falling to the floor! And I see a trail of them leading from in front of the Y2K testing lab. Chuck, you clean up the broken plates. Slim, you take the paper you're holding and wipe up those specks."

"But Arkey, these papers are a manuscript, ready for the archives. I'll get a mop, instead."

"Manuscript? Look. Just blank pages! Wait a minute!" You came by the Y2K test lab just now. Here, let me check these things on the floor."

THE MYSTERY SOLVED

Arkey knelt, ran his hand over the dark trail, and examined the many objects that clung to his palm. "Why, these are letters of the alphabet! Here're c's, t's, h's, i's, and an s." He rose. His face darkened as he swatted away a host of b's, z's, g's, o's, and p's still floating, defying gravity as they were swirled around the room by a breeze from an open window.

"You guys clean up your mess. Oh, man, just wait till Vern gets back. You're going to get a cussing out like never before. It's taken a week to get this stuff ready for printing. I'd hate to be in *your* shoes! Think I know what caused this. I'm going down to the ink shop and talk with Inky."

He raced to the ink shop and confronted Inky. "Inky, now think. I believe your instructions for that boating book stated that "Page-Fix+" was to be mixed with the usual ink, at a ratio of 1:4. Am I right?"

"Exactly! But we've got a new man, Gordon, mixing the inks now. Let's talk with him about this." They walked to the ink mixing area in the back room, where Gordon was grinding chemicals for later production use.

"Gordon, we've had a problem with the ink used in our last job, #428K, that boating book we're about to print. Did you mix "Page-Fix+" into the ink for that job? The entire manuscript has disappeared."

Gordon's face lighted with glee. A maniacal laugh, more a howl, filled the room. "Ha, ha, ha!! He got what he deserved!" The pan of powdered chemicals he'd been grinding lay nearby. In one quick move he grabbed it, threw the powder at them, and turned to run. Both ducked to escape the gray, lung-clogging dust. As Gordon ran for the door, Arkey downed him with a classic open-field tackle.

"All right, you got me. I'll confess. I'm Gordon Uplate, former CEO and owner of *New Generation Books,* now in bankruptcy. The author of that boating book caused my downfall by using parts of a letter I'd written to him as an endorsement for his book, which was far from my intention. I was laughed out of the business! Lost all my customers, and no one has signed with me since. I'd heard rumors of Dr. Pufmeister's research, and formulated a plan for revenge when I heard the author was here at Happy Hills. And now, the plates are gone! His entire manuscript gone, destroyed by the evil influences of the Y2K testing on it before it could be fixed with "Page-Fix+!" My revenge is complete!"

Catching Inky and Arkey by surprise, he dashed to a shelf, took out a jar labeled "Page-Fix+" and guzzled the dark liquid down in an instant. Dropping the jar, he glared at the men, smiled triumphantly, and fell to the floor.

There it is. The entire unembellished story, as it happened. We attempted to resurrect the hilarious blooper stories from the letters that were netted in midair and swept up off the floor, but found quickly that it was impossible to glue them onto paper in such a manner that made sense, to say nothing of the time it would have taken. The original price of the book has been reduced by 79 cents as a result of this omission. Fortunately for you readers, I had a duplicate copy of the rest of the book in my cell, away from the corrosive forces of Y2K testing, which enabled us to get the book to you in its present form. I *did* have it printed with "Page-Fix+," so it will NOT suffer the same fate as the missing chapter when the witching hour arrives December 31.

In retrospect, I guess it *is* my fault, for wronging Gordon in the first place, that the blooper chapter is not here. As a sop to you, I will present, as best I can remember, a summation of several, to alleviate the heartache and frustration I know you are feeling by not being able to snicker, chuckle, or guffaw at the hilarity you were expecting to find:

1. Crewman, being hoisted to the top of a 40-foot mast in a bosun's chair to repair a masthead light, panics and freezes in place, unwilling to move any direction. A rescuer, reaching for him, looks down and also freezes in place. For all we know, they're both still there, being fed by helicopter.

2. Cruising dog, visiting a specially constructed sawdust box on the foredeck to do his toilet routine, does what dogs always have been known to do afterwards, namely, pretending to bury their droppings by kicking with hind legs. In this case, the entire contents of the box, sawdust *and the droppings,* are kicked back into the cockpit area, scattering a group of guests drinking cocktails.

3. Tourist in China, mistakenly believing a Chinese junk is a place for garbage, throws remains of chop suey dinner down into the boat, starting a Tong War against tourists.

4. Tourists on Nile cruise, far upriver, decide to dive off boat on hot day to swim in crocodile-infested waters. No refunds are given to the heirs of the deceased.

5. New boater lights match to cast light into gas tank to determine amount of fuel remaining. Hasn't been found yet.

6. An inland-lake boater, mooring for the first time in tidal waters, ties bow line to a piling instead of the cleat on the dock. Discovers error when entire family slides out of bunks as they lie sleeping that night when the tide goes out.

7. An unsuspecting guest aboard a boat in the Chittenden Locks in Seattle releases stern line *first,* when departing after locking procedure, allowing boat to be carried entire length of locks *back-wards*, accompanied by much finger pointing, cheering and jeering by hundreds of tourists lining the observation decks.

8. Crewman, going forward to foredeck to drop spinnaker, releases wrong line at wrong time, suddenly finds himself holding the spinnaker in a death grip *out over the water and ahead of the boat* after a sudden, severe wind gust hits.

9. Sober boater sets national record by falling from his dinghy nine times in a single boating season as he attempts to board his boat from the dinghy.

10. Frightened cruising cat claws and climbs 37-foot wooden mast and won't come down.

11. New boat owner, wondering what a certain bolt in aft cockpit area is for, loosens it, causing the boat's rudder to descend 80 feet to the lake bottom.

12. A fishing plug, cast by boater from stern of his boat, is chased, caught, and hooked by a very large seagull.

13 Entire unit of boat, trailer, and car rolls backwards and disappears into lake at launch site as driver leaves car to untie boat from trailer.

14. Eighteen-foot runabout, traveling 55 miles per hour, slips off trailer onto highway, after the owner used unsuccessful bowline to secure boat to trailer.

15. Seattle boat owner stacks load of iron pipe near deck navigation station, reversing north and south on compass. On evening trip, he ends up in Olympia instead of Bellingham, his original destination, now some 150 miles away.

You get the idea. But in looking at these, I find they're not so hilarious after all. Do this: (NOT Browsers!) Take a black felt pen and cross out the words "World's Most Hilarious," leaving just the more realistic "Boating Bloopers."

EPILOGUE

After the droll events you have just read about were over, I found I could not let my conscience continue to gnaw at me without taking some kind of action. While contacting Gordon Uplate's family to let them know I would buy a lovely, large, marble headstone for his grave, I was amazed to find he was not only alive, but more than well. Apparently "Page-Fix+" contains an ingredient affecting muscle growth in adults.

Gordon, when I met him upon my release from Happy Hills, was sprouting muscles upon muscles. He is in training for the next Olympic Games as a weight lifter, and assured me he would be the gold medal winner in the heavyweight, unlimited division. Now weighing 235 pounds, up from the 145 pounds he weighed as a book executive, he has already jerked 925 pounds with *one* hand, and recently pressed 1,300 pounds with both, all world records. He cautioned me not to tell about the effects of "Page-Fix+" on his physical development, worrying that if word gets out, the Olympic Health Testing Committee will develop tests for detection of this newest performance enhancer, make it illegal to use, and rob him of the right to compete. He and Dr. Pufmeister have joined as partners to market "Page-Fix+" to the sports world, but were bought out by a professional football team, the name to remain anonymous, paying the twosome $35,000,000 for exclusive use of the product.

However, here's a clue for you to watch for next football season. When you see one team throwing 300-350 pound opponents around on the field like beach balls, you'll know why, having read it here first. Look for Gordon Uplate, ferocious linebacker, to become the first pro-bowl all star in his *rookie* year, and amazingly, after *no* backyard, peewee, junior high, high school, or college football experience, except as a fan! Only in America!

".. STAY IF YA' _WANT_ - BUT WE'RE _DESERTIN'._.... THIS SKIPPER THINKS RULES-OF-THE-ROAD ARE JUST FER CARS!"

A LEGAL LETTER OF ADVICE

LAW OFFICES
of
FORTRESS LEGAL SERVICES
"You make 'em. We guard 'em"
Specialists in Copyright, Trademark, Patent, and International Law

Dear Bill:

Thank you for submitting to us, for our comments, your detailed plans for marketing your book, *Boating-Exposed!*. By having taken this step, we can save you from some serious errors if you follow our suggestions. Our legal opinions follow, point by point, the questions you asked:

Point #1 - Yes, it is legal to write and publish your book under an assumed name, what is known as a pseudonym, or pen name. Many authors, men *and* women, do this regularly. In your case, after reading the book, we recommend it highly.

Point #2 - Your statement that you may legally change your name is somewhat surprising to us. You can, to save expense associated with that move, simply make up a pseudonym and notify the publishing house of your decision. No legal name change is necessary. However, as in the case of the pseudonym mentioned in Point #1, you might consider this as a prudent move before the book becomes public.

Point #3 - While you do have every right to legally change your name, do NOT, under ANY circumstances, change it to Tom Clancy, Stephen King, Maeve Binchy, Jane Austen *or any other famous author, living or dead!* While we here at Fortress realize that any of these famous names listed as author on *your* book would automatically result in it becoming a bestseller, we here, by a vote of 11-9, feel that such a step might be considered slightly unethical. It could also result in a lawsuit of some sort, except for Ms. Austen, who, unfortunately, is no longer writing. Besides, Bill, readers would quickly see, probably by no later than page two, that *your* book, with its highlights being letters and numbers falling off pages by December 31 and talk of angry anchors rising up to take over our planet, is simply not written in the same style as any of the aforementioned authors.

For example, the male authors mentioned, with their tightly written, well-researched, action-filled, thrilling stories, peopled by heroic protagonists and evil, barbarous villains, usually write *one* complete story of 500-900 pages, as compared with your many brief short stories and sketches. The female authors mentioned write of love and romance, appealing to women, and with a growing number of male readers. The closest *you* have come to an appealing women's story is your chapter on sandworm and beach flea recipes, which we feel may have a limited appeal in today's book market.

It's possible that by page three of your book, most readers will have decided to return it to the bookstore for a refund, and, even worse, to begin a boycott of the bookstore until all copies of it have been removed, and quite possibly burned. Other legal name changes you mentioned as possibilities—Charles Dickens and Arthur Conan Doyle come to mind—are also on the taboo list. Few book buyers would believe that they are still writing. Your idea of using Mathew, M.L. John was a clever idea, but even though those four helped write the best seller of all time, we doubt if they'd have the drawing power in today's mass media markets. If you decide to use *that* as a pseudonym, better give Mark and Luke due credit by using their full names, not just their initials. We advise against that idea also.

Point #4 - While you are right in pursuing the female market, none of us feel you should use a female pseudonym. Yes we know many women writers use male pseudonyms, usually to gain wider acceptance of their having written what would ordinarily be thought of as a male-written, action/adventure book. While many female characters appear in your book, your stories carry the stamp of a male author. Be yourself!

Point #5 - In reply to your most significant question, and read our comment carefully, NO! NO! It is NOT necessary to have a sex-change operation, termed a gender alteration in our business, to be able to legally use a female pseudonym. DON'T DO IT! We know of no women authors who have been altered to male status in order to use a male pseudonym. There may be some, but we don't know and *don't want to know* about this kind of thing! It's none of *our* business!

We here at Fortress Legal Services have enjoyed helping you in your quest for legal answers and somewhat enjoyed reading the book you sent as a sample. If we can be of service later, please call. P.S.-Your check is now overdue. Please remit promptly by return mail or face litigation.

Sincerely yours,

Rod

Rodney Pilfrey

P.S. #2 - Bill, you might consider changing your chapter on recipes to add carrying a small-mesh net when lost. Last week at the beach I tried catching a beach flea by hand, but couldn't. Those little devils are fast! Luckily we had a picnic hamper along, so our whole family survived, but without a net I probably would have died of overexertion rather then of starvation. Frankly, I'm glad I was unsuccessful. They didn't look very appetizing. *R.*

STARBOARD CLIPPER

MEANINGFUL EXCERPTS FROM
THE SECRETARY'S MINUTES:
FINAL MEETING OF THE
INTERNATIONAL LEXICOGRAPHICAL SOCIETY

Author's Note: It has been estimated that 72% of the readers of *Boating-Exposed!* will wonder why the minutes of this learned society have been included in a book purportedly related to boating. The other 28% will realize that boating *does* have its own vocabulary, many of these words actually being found in existing dictionaries - words such as water, boat, ship, deck, compass, engine, anchor, tide, tidal wave, capsize, oars, ahoy, and Help!, among others. The fact is that reality often defies rational thought and good sense, hence this chapter that proves the truth just stated.

You may not learn much about boating from this chapter. For the avid and compulsive reader, consider this as optional reading, to be read after *all* other reading material in your home has been exhausted, but *before* being reduced to reading the advertising material on cereal boxes, bread wrappers, and the current letter from the IRS notifying you that you made a VERY LARGE error on your tax return and now owe over $3,200, plus penalties (more, for some!). I have taken the liberty of adding to the secretary's minutes certain information which you will find sprinkled here and there throughout the chapter, enclosed in parentheses. I was fortunate enough to observe the proceedings on USBC-TV, Jim Nolsen and new anchor Penelope Airey handling the telecast. It was highly exciting! Too bad you missed it.

"Jim Nolsen here for USBC-TV, with our latest addition to the news coverage staff, Penelope Airey. Today we bring to you the final meeting of the International Standard Lexicographical Society. For those of you who have been following the progress of this prestigious society for the past 27 years, as its members worked preparing the *New International Standard Dictionary,* you will realize today is their F Day, F for final finish, wrapping up for closure and publication.

It has been a difficult 27 years, with lexicographers from every country in the world contributing words, definitions, and ideas to this mammoth work. We're here in the auditorium of Wordsmith University, whose graduates comprise 98% of the world's lexicographers, 63% of America's college English professors, and tens of thousands of translators, editorial consultants, and proofreaders. Curiously, Wordsmith U. is also the home of the 'Fighting Amanuenses' (that is, those who write or copy words), whose stunning 49-7 victory in the Eggplant Bowl on January 1 earned them the national championship in football. Wordsmith U. is very proud of one of its former fullbacks, Clarence 'Toughie' Randon, who, after gaining 6,400 yards in his four years at Wordsmith, contributed a new word to dictionaries, 'Duh.' An All-American his final year of play, he was the last athlete in America to play all four years without a helmet. For those who would like to visit 'Toughie', call the Wordsmith U. Hospital for visiting hours.

The researchers have begun filing into the auditorium. The committees who worked together will sit together. For example, those who researched Ba-B0 will be together, the Te-Ty group together, and so on. While we're waiting for the meeting to begin, here's Penelope with a special feature on why today's meeting is so significant in light of past history. Penelope, you're on, live."

Thanks, Jim. Are words and spelling important? Yes! Is that enough, Jim, or should I develop the idea more?"

"Go for it, Penelope. We have three or four minutes to fill, so do elaborate on your 'Yes' theme."

"Thanks, Jim. Yes, words, their spellings and definitions are crucial for personal and business success. Without words we'd just make growling and grunting sounds, with these animal-like sounds open to wide interpretation. And even *with* words there are possibilities for misunderstandings. Take the case of King Obwander, a mid-eastern potentate in 870 B.C. As an important religious ceremony neared, he ordered his royal chamberlain, Prince Wandober, to put out a royal edict that, because of a shortage of sheep that year, only goats were to be used for sacrifices in the ceremonies. Prince Wandober, known to the people to be two deenahs short of a full dahneel, printed the edict, with goat, unfortunately, spelled as 'goate.' This was taken by the people, after long serious debates at meetings set up to ascertain the true meaning of 'goate,' to be understood as 'goatee'. Before the error was brought to King Obwander's attention, 32% of the goateed male population and 8% of the goateed females had ended up, much to their displeasure, as sacrifices to their supreme god, Upigh. Upigh, accustomed to eating goats and sheep at the ceremonies, did not care for this new taste, and cast plagues upon the king and his people. Prince Wandober was condemned to stand in a corner for the rest of his life. So, you see how important it is to spell properly. But Jim, there was a successful conclusion to this story. Upigh wandered and swam to what is now America, where he made his fortune designing and selling cedar-bark loin cloths to the local natives, who heretofore had been accustomed to wearing only paper bags over their heads so no one would see who they were seeing naked."

"Uhhhh...thanks so much, Penelope. We've learned so much from you today. The lexicographers are all seated in their sections and...there's the gavel! Oh! That was a mighty blow by the chairman. Many of those closest to him are shaking their fists; others are adjusting their hearing aids and screaming in pain! Professor Whiteson, the chairman, has been on loan to the project from Her Majesty's Royal College of Linguistic Purity in London England, for the past 27 years, and has been a driving force."

"Come to order! Sorry about that gavel. Good afternoon, fellow lexicographers. It's good to see you here. I understand that of the original group of 3,200 who began the project 27 years ago, 2,135 of us are still alive, and close to publishing the fruits of our efforts, the *First International Standard Dictionary of the World's Nations!* (Cascades of applause, except for a group initiating a petition to sue Prof. Whiteson for damage to eardrums.) This is a happy occasion for us all, as now we can finally return to our families once again, after globe-hopping to ensure that all peoples of the world are represented in our new tome. And to those professionals who said it couldn't be done, I say *'Piffle'*to them!!!(piffle, pif'fle n. Trifling talk or action; stuff and nonsense-pif'fle, int.)

"Jim Nolsen here again. As Professor Whiteson exclaimed 'Piffle', another series of cheers fills the hall. Many of the assembled are shocked by his use of 'piffle' to admonish the academicians in other fields of knowledge who have continually heaped scorn on

175

any thought of this group's possibility of success. The word is the strongest insult a degreed linguist can suffer, stronger even than words commonly employed by angry linguists, such as humbug, hoaxer, harlequin, merry-andrew, nitwit, booby, dupe or fellow, when insulting one another. Back to Prof Whiteson."

"This nonpareil task has been totally completed (wild cheering)...except for the He-Ho committee, which has come to a total impasse over a definition of just *one* word in their assigned field, which keeps them from completion. (Boos, hisses and groans well up in the hall.) I will introduce Professor Andrew Malworde, chairman of the He-Ho group, who will explain the problem. Professor Malworde."

"Thank you, Professor Whiteson. My dear colleagues, to make the committee's 27-year-old argument short and to the point, the word in question is 'Head'...H...E...A...D. To the 36 definitions found in standard dictionaries we have added ten more. (Scattered cheers) The problem is a diversity of opinion over the inclusion of head as 'a small room or station for disposal of human digestive and urinary waste aboard a boat.' To use the word in this fashion did not set well with half our committee, with the 10-10 vote precluding it from being accepted as a definition. It was felt by half that the word has too many *noble* connotations, such as the head being the seat of all human emotion, the leader of something, or the foam in a glass or stein of well-brewed beer. With these uplifting definitions in mind, they also felt that the head on a boat, usually ill-smelling, leaking and too odious in nature to be grouped with such quality definitions as the examples above, should not be mentioned at all. (More wild cheering from the attendees.) Now, I'm American and a boater. In America, it's usual to call the toilet in a boat the 'head,' but those opposed also claim that the inclusion of this nautical definition would sow confusion in the minds of people everywhere.

For example, would a headmaster of a school be known as the custodian who made sure the toilet and bowl were cleaned? Would a headdress be worn by women answering Nature's call? There is no toilet in a car, yet it has headlights. Must we change wrestling terminology to avoid use of the common headlock used by wrestlers? Will that make people stop eating the delicacy, head cheese? When dead and buried, a corpse would no longer need a headstone, being no longer necessary, except in the case of a live burial. The committee's problem is analogous to throwing a pebble into a pond. As the pebble hits the water, waves radiate evenly away from the point of impact. If this new nautical definition of 'head' is accepted as a boat toilet, think of all the other words with 'head' in them that must be changed to avoid the total collapse of the Hea- sections of present and future dictionaries. (Sustained applause, whistling, some boos from the American spectators in the upper gallery.) We looked at alternative uses and discarded most out-of-hand.

One can't say going to the bathroom on a boat, because most boats don't have bathtubs. One shouldn't say, "I'm going to the restroom" on a boat, as most fellow passengers would think you were at least slightly crazy to believe you could rest more comfortably on a cramped toilet seat in the tiny cubicle provided than on the comfortable cushions available to you in the main cabin. Women, used to leaving for the ladies' room by saying they're going to freshen up or powder their noses, would have to find some other name for their destination, on a boat, rather than mention some embarrassingly crudity of a term."

"Jim Nolsen again. Professor Malworde has paused for a sip of water. The hall is buzzing with excitement as the assemblage, mostly in their 70s, 80s and 90s, begins to sense there will be a vote on this issue. A few are waving their canes and crutches in anger as disputes break out, and one researcher is...yes, he's so angry he's wheeling himself out of the auditorium. Back to Professor Malworde."

"Order, please. Thank you. To continue, the committee members visited every country and found that there are some commonalties that we are considering. We found that the Greek 'tooahletah,' the Japanese 'toheereh,' the Polish 'toaletorwz,' and the Italian 'toalette' sound similar to the American 'toilet,' having the same root. However, the Russian 'oobohrnuhyuk,' the Spanish 'el servicio,' and the Romanian 'WC' have different etymologies. Many undeveloped countries had no name for toilet, merely digging holes in the ground for disposal. The committee does have a recommendation as a word to replace 'head' as the toilet designation on a boat. It is short, easily remembered, simply spelled, except for some American politicians who'd probably add an 'e' at the end, and is already in use. It is the English 'loo.' The committee could see only one major problem, in that the Japanese would probably pronounce it 'roo' instead, and..."

"OBJECTION! OBJECTION!"

"I recognize the colleague with the suspenders."

"Si Aplnok, from Washington State, here. We MUST NOT adopt 'loo' as the name for a boat toilet, especially with an 'e' at the end of it. The State of Washington's official rock song is 'Louie, Louie.' If 'loo' is adopted, for over 2,000,000 Washingtonians, it would be like singing 'Toilet, toilet!' For all people in my state, I say this is completely unacceptable!"

"Thank you Mr. Aplnok. Would the secretary please enter his remarks into the minutes? Thank you. I now recognize the colleague in the green dress."

"I'm Dr. Megan Sandusty, committee chair of the Ca-Ci study group and a resident of Australia. If 'loo' is adopted, rather than 'head' for a boat toilet, it will present serious public relations and sanitation problems in Sydney and other Australian port cities being visited by Japanese tourists. If they need a toilet in town and say 'roo' rather than 'loo,' our kindhearted citizens will probably direct them to the town's zoo, to see what we Aussies call 'roos, short for kangaroos. While I don't believe the visitors will mistake the 'roo for a 'loo,' just think of some *very* uncomfortable tourists before the matter becomes straightened out. We don't wish any ill will engendered by this problem."

"Thank you, Ms. Sandusty. Secretary, please enter her remarks into the minutes. Thank you."

"PROFESSOR MALWORDE! THE FLOOR, PLEASE!"

"The chair recognizes you. Proceed, please."

"Reginald Brookstone, secretary of the Oa-Om committee, from London. All this talk of heads, seats, loos, 'roos, rest rooms, toilets, powder rooms and bathrooms! All for what? 27 years of devilishly difficult work held up because you bloody Yanks can't tell your heads from your seats!!!"

"Easy, Brookstone. Rein in your emotions. Just you do remember what happened to General Cornwallis in 1781!"

"Eh? Oh...right. Sorry, old chap. I have a plan for consideration and possible vote to bring this meeting to an end. We don't want another 27 years deciding it! You said there are now 46 definitions for the word 'head.' Let's add another to make it 47. Listen to this proposal for a final fit: Head (hed), n. (American-vulgar) slang, small, cubicled room used as a toilet on a boat. syn. loo, powder room, bathroom."

"Dr. Hisingh Cobera, India, here. I second the motion!"

"Dr. Cobera, I'm not sure that was a..."

"Jim Nolsen again. The hall has erupted! Ear-splitting cheers from this geriatric crowd out-shout the supporters of the original definition. On my right, 20 or so gray-haired wheelchair-bound lexicographers and linguists have charged against their opponents, backed by the support of 30-40 oldsters with canes and crutches swinging wildly. The opponents have been backed completely out an exit door, and are in disarray on the lawn outside. The police, alerted earlier when it appeared the opponents might begin a riotous showdown, have barricaded the doors and now have the situation under control. There are no casualties, unless one counts the occasional broken canes resulting from duels fought by opponents. What's this, Penelope?"

"Jim, a note handed to me from Professor Malworde and co-signed by Professor Whiteson."

"Thanks. Let me read it to the viewers. 'We believe this demonstration shows strong support for what we declare to be an official, legal vote for Dr. Brookstone's idea, even if not originally presented as a motion. The citizens of most countries of the world will continue calling their toilets whatever they called them before today's meeting. That's all right. But in America, if any of you are boating with either of us and are answering Nature's call by heading towards a small cubicle containing a porcelain toilet bowl with a seat on it, just go, and call it anything you bloody well please. Just don't tell either of us.' (signed) Professor Whiteson and Professor Malworde. There you have it, the official outcome of this long-awaited event. Outside, noisy groups of Wordsmith University's undergraduates, attracted by the commotion and the arrival of 15 police cars, are carrying both Professor Brookstone and Dr. Cobera on their shoulders down the main campus way. In the auditorium hallway, there are two long lines of fidgeting lexicographers standing outside the doors of the...I don't know *what* to call them anymore. But one door says 'MEN' and the other 'WOMEN.' This is Jim Nolsen, with Penelope Airey, for USBC-TV, signing off. We hope you have enjoyed today's show."

SALTY DOG

TO THE OMITTED READER

You have finished reading *Boating-Exposed!* You now realize the process of parodying and satirizing groups is a difficult and thought-provoking endeavor. The author has made every effort to include as large a number of groups as possible to make the book more personalized and closer to you. The realization is that a larger number of groups should have been included, but were unfortunately left out due to the page limitations.

A solution has been developed that it is hoped will be satisfactory to all, but mainly to prevent lawsuits due to a particular group having been omitted. Please read the following alphabetical groups fortunate enough to have been included in this first printing. If you or your group are *not* on the list and wish to be included in the second printing, clip out the Inclusion Form I following the list, fill it out, and send it to the author at the Happy Hills Hospital and Rest Home within 30 days following your purchase of the book. There is no charge.

Alcoholics, Aliens (space), Americans, Boaters (both sail and power), Babylonians, Boat Salesmen and Boat Supply Salesmen, CEOs, Censors, County Councils, Editors, Egyptians, English teachers, French (the), Garbage Scow Operators, Geoducks, Germans (the), Historians, Housewives, Human Beings, Inventors, Italians (the), Japanese (the), Judges, Lawyers, Landlubbers, Leif Ericsson, Lexicographers, Men, Non-Drinkers, Norwegians (the), Olympia (city of), Police, Parents, Poor (the), Polish (the), Psychiatrists, Psychologists, Publishers, Racers (boat), Rich (the) Romanians (the), Russian Tsars, Sickly (the), Road Ragers, Rock Bands, Safari Gun Bearers, Sasquatch, Scientists, Steelhead, Students, Supreme Court Justices, Tooth Fairies, TV Commentators, Ex-U-boat Kommanders, Washington State, Women, Women (lightly clad), Workers, Writers, Yacht Clubs, Y2K Doomsayers.

While examining the list, you may find yourself in two or more categories, in which case you would not qualify for inclusion in the second printing. Look carefully.

INCLUSION FORM I

Dear Bill:

I cannot find a listing that applies to my group or myself, and I'd like the chance to be roasted, parodied, satirized, or insulted by you in the second printing of *Boating-Exposed!*

Name of group_____

Specific reason(s) me or my group should be included: (100 words or less-any more and you will be disqualified!)

Type of action to be taken by author: Circle ONE choice only!

Simple Mention, Parody, Satire, Irony, Roast, Insult

_____

Signature   Date

THE LATE-BREAKING NEWS

"Good afternoon, viewers. Penelope Airey here with the late afternoon news for USBC-TV. Today's lead story is an update on yesterday's discovery of the huge asteroid hurtling towards planet Earth. Traveling at 38,000 miles per hour, and some 987,000,000 miles away, the 87-mile-diameter space rock will impact Earth in approximately six months, annihilating all life as we know it, as dust from the impact enters and circles our atmosphere, cutting off all sunlight for years. El Crashero, as it has been named by the Mexican astronomers who discovered it, could instead land in one of our oceans. The water, heated to 18,000 degrees Centigrade by contact with El Crashero, would cause extinction by parboiling the population and all plant and animal life.

All other observatories have been attempting to pinpoint the unfriendly intruder. Both the U.S. Senate and House of Representatives are considering appointing committees to study this phenomenon next month after returning from recess, and our President has called for a meeting of heads of state in Hawaii next month. However, Russia, China, North Korea, Iran, Iraq, and Afghanistan have indicated they will boycott this meeting on the grounds that the U.S., having taken the initiative regarding the emergency, is simply using it as a poor excuse to spread its influence throughout the world. The President will mobilize all units of the National Guard to...What, Jim?"

"Penelope, an important scientific communiqué has just been received here at the station. We interrupt this newscast to go to our TV affiliate station on beautiful San Grande Island, where Professor Merton Strawbridge, author, inventor and leading-edge Y2K facilitator with his newest invention of *"Page-Fix,"* and non-pareil DNA researcher, will be interviewed by me. He claims to have significant documents, which he will televise to the public for the first time. Professor, can you hear us?"

"Yes, Jim. Thanks for allowing me to share my discovery with the world. It couldn't come at a better time. Who knows? Perhaps it will help save enough people from the upcoming disaster to re-populate Earth."

"Professor, what is the nature of your work?"

"I've been working for the past four years trying to answer the most pressing and baffling question facing people today. It also has perplexed philosophers and scientists since time immemorial. It is related to my DNA research and answers conclusively the question, 'Why doesn't *everyone* own a boat?" The question has been laid to rest following my research. I now own the patent for a medical break-through that will allow *anyone who wants one* to own a boat, subject, of course, to space availability in marinas."

"This IS big news! Please explain in laymen's terms."

"Yes. I'll keep it as simple as possible. Every human is endowed with DNA, genes, and chromosomes that belong to that individual *only.* There are not two people in the world who share the same characteristics. By taking samples from over 6,000 boaters who have landed here on the island, we have been able to analyze their DNA to discover how boater DNA differs from that of landlubbers, which we have also analyzed. For example, here is a typical DNA strand from a landlubber, as seen under our powerful electron microscopes, which is labelled Figure #1. The small crosshatchings are the genes, each one of which controls some vital life function at some stage of de-velopment of a human fetus. Genes are the objects that make a person unique, a one-of-a-kind, so to speak. All the pictures shown here have been magnified nearly 10,000 times. Each gene in the strand has been given its own number. There are hundreds of thousands, so we have much work yet to be done to know what each gene controls. It's fantastic work!"

Figure #1 - Gene patterns of a landlubber:

600   700   800

Now compare that gene with that of a typical boater. Pay particular attention to gene #764.

Figure #2 - Gene pattern of the typical sailboater:

184

You will notice that the gene, which we have labelled #b764, the b representing boat, has mutated from normal, foreordaining him or her to a life under sail.

Figure #3 - Gene pattern of a typical powerboater:

The possessor of this gene is at present age 55, and the owner of a 64-foot ocean cruiser. He, like the sailboater in Figure #2, is hereditarily bound by this mutated gene, to be the owner of a large powerboat. Anyone holding this mutation is powerless to stop the urge to own a boat. We have further subdivided the genes due to our research: #bs764 is a sailboat, #bp 764 is a powerboat, #bc764 a canoe, #bi 764 an inflatable, #bt 764 a tug, #bu764 a umiak, #bj764 a junk, and so forth, for every type of boat found afloat. We have even resurrected a bireme from the eastern Mediterranean, labeling it #bb764, but so far have not been able to collect DNA samples from any of the ancients who sailed and rowed in them. But when we do, we're 100% sure the pattern of the individual will appear as we have drawn it up. There is no uncertainty. We can even tell from the DNA of a newborn if it will be a windsurfer, and have assigned #bws764 as a sub-gene for its eventual appearance."

"Professor, this is amazing scientific research! Do you have other news, especially as it relates to El Crashero? You had mentioned something earlier on the telecast."

"Jim, by means of a non-invasive laser zap we can now eliminate a normal #764 and transplant into a person, who wants to be a boater, a #b764 of any type that person wishes to own at some time in the future. And for boat owners who wish to lose the powerful urge to own a boat, we can also zap the #b764 gene so they can get out of boating with no regrets. For those in the Sahara, Gobi, and other desert areas, the American Great Plains, and mountainous areas that have no proper boating areas, we can eliminate the terrible yearnings to own a boat. This is a major breakthrough, as there is untold sadness, frustration, depression, and even suicide among people who unknowingly had the #b764 gene and were plagued with these symptoms. This will reduce medical costs and expenses by 40%, as well as eliminating most autopsies in which the cause of death is uncertain. The coroners can start by examining #764 to see if it's a #b764 of some type that the deceased unknowingly possessed."

"Professor, San Grande is such a remote island. How can you claim that over 6,000 boaters landed there and were tested?"

"Jim, most of them were lost boaters with uncompensated compasses, road maps instead of marine charts, and with no sure idea in mind where they were or where they were going. They'd land on our beaches, scrounge around for food, and then gladly submit to our testing program in exchange for hot meals and a shower. Our native sand worms, starfish, beach fleas, clams, crabs, porcupines, tree bark, and plants were almost wiped out by lost, starving boaters who'd run out of food. One fellow even swam out and climbed onto the back of a whale basking on the surface, but he couldn't bite through the skin to the blubber. We finally posted signs on all the beaches directing lost boaters here to Happy Hills."

"Professor, you mentioned your work might help save civilization after El Crashero hits. Can you be more specific as to how this might happen?"

"Yes. With the gene research we've done here, we may be able to fit fish-gill genes onto human DNA strands to enable people to live underwater to avoid the dust in case the asteroid hits on land. In case it's a water hit, we could develop replacement genes from camels and fit them into a person's genes. Camels, as you know, have a fantastic ability to resist sandstorms on the desert that may prove useful for human survival. We have six months to try to develop appropriate measures. We're working hard at it."

"Good luck! If you succeed, you'll put San Grande Island on the map."

"Jim, it's already on the map. You remember Gordon Uplate, who won three different weight-lifting records at the last Olympics and later starred as all-pro running back and linebacker in his team's Superbowl win? He spent some time here. He donated half his signing bonus to the Happy Hills Research Center, now established. It enabled us to get the equipment and supplies to carry out our research. Some of the world's greatest scientists have applied to work here in the most modern facilities to be found on Earth."

"Professor Strawbridge, your talents know no bounds."

"Jim, I must interrupt to give our listeners the late-breaking news, the latest on El Crashero! It's so important, to prevent hysteria, rioting, breaking windows, overturning cars, looting, and setting arson fires!"

"Go ahead, Penelope. Hope it's not getting here quicker than anyone suspects!"

"It came in while you were interviewing Professor Strawbridge. I'll read the message. It's from the staff of the Muy Alto Observatory, discoverers of El Crashero. 'To all caballeros and senoritas: Our deepest apologies for the anguish we may have put you through for the past two days. A sticky weed seed, blown by the severe wind and sticking to the outer lens of our telescope and magnified by that lens, caused some of the more excitable astronomers here to misinterpret it as a gigantic asteroid heading on a collision course with our beloved planet. For all those who have already jumped off cliffs and high buildings, we offer utmost sympathy. (signed) The Staff-Muy Alto Montana."

"Jim Nolsen and Penelope Airey here, signing off for the latest-breaking news at USBC-TV. Good night."

"Well, Jim, what a relief! No El Crashero! I was so worried last night when the reports came out, I couldn't sleep. I'm going home and go to bed. What are you going to do?"

"Penelope, I'm going to the airport and buy a ticket for San Grande Island. Professor Strawbridge may be eccentric, to say the least, but if what he told us tonight is true, I'm going to become the proud owner of the most beautiful boat I've thought about for years. But first I'm going to get #764 tested to see whether I'm a #bs764 or a #bp764. I just hope it's not a #bi764 or a #bu764. Good night, Penelope, and sweet dreams to you all."

187

IT DOESN'T GET ANY BETTER

INDEX

To order more copies of *Boating-Exposed!*
or for more information about Puget Sound Press,
contact:

**Puget Sound Press
6523 California Ave., SW
PMB 292
Seattle, WA 98136
http://www.pugetsoundpress.com
email: thezo@sprintmail.com**